Practical Problems in Mathematics

FOR

Graphic Arts

Practical Problems in Mathematics

FOR

Graphic Arts

LaVONNE VERMEERSCH
CHARLES SOUTHWICK

10 9 8 7

LIBRARY OF CONGRESS CATALOG CARD NUMBER: 82-72128
ISBN: 0-8273-2100-7

Printed in the United States of America
Published simultaneously in Canada
by Nelson Canada,
A division of The Thomson Corporation

DELMAR PUBLISHERS INC.
2 COMPUTER DRIVE, WEST — BOX 15-015
ALBANY, NEW YORK 12212

PREFACE

The student learning graphic arts theory must be familiar with terminology and practices. PRACTICAL PROBLEMS IN MATHEMATICS FOR GRAPHIC ARTS provides the student with practical and realistic mathematical problems which are encountered. By solving the problems, the technical and mathematical aspects are both strengthened, thus providing a solid foundation for a career as a graphic arts technician.

PRACTICAL PROBLEMS IN MATHEMATICS FOR GRAPHIC ARTS is one in a series of workbooks which can be used in conjunction with a comprehensive mathematics textbook—such as APPLIED GENERAL MATHEMATICS or BASIC MATHEMATICS SIMPLIFIED (Delmar Publishers)—or in an individualized math program for students with interests in specific fields. Each workbook provides practical experiences in using mathematical principles to solve occupationally related problems.

This series of workbooks is designed for use by a wide range of students. The workbooks are suitable for any student from the junior high school level through high school and up to the two-year college level. These workbooks, though designed for the vocational student, are equally suitable for the liberal arts student.

The series has many benefits for the instructor and for the student. For the student, the workbooks offer a step-by-step approach to the mastery of essential skills in mathematics. Each workbook includes relevant and easily understandable problems in a specific vocational field.

For the instructor, the series offers a coherent and concise approach to the teaching of mathematical skills. Each workbook is complemented by an instructor's guide which includes answers to every problem in the workbook and solutions to many of the problems. The instructor's guide also includes references to comprehensive mathematics textbooks published by Delmar Publishers. In addition, two achievement reviews are provided at the end of each workbook to provide an effective means of measuring the student's progress.

Both the instructor and the student will benefit from the specific vocational material and the appendix materials such as performing the basic operations with denominate numbers.

Other workbooks in this series are:

PRACTICAL PROBLEMS IN MATHEMATICS FOR

AUTOMOTIVE TECHNICIANS	MACHINISTS
CARPENTERS	MASONS
CONSUMERS	MECHANICAL DRAFTING
COSMETOLOGY	OFFICE WORKERS
ELECTRONICS TECHNICIANS	SHEET METAL TECHNICIANS
ELECTRICIANS	THE METRIC SYSTEM
HEATING AND COOLING TECHNICIANS	WELDERS

CONTENTS

Contents

Unit 1 ADDITION OF WHOLE NUMBERS

BASIC PRINCIPLES

- Apply the principles of addition to the printing and graphic communications industry by solving the practical problems in this unit.

PRACTICAL PROBLEMS

1. A certain number of hours are required to produce a printing job. The paste-up artist works 17 hours on the mechanicals. Office corrections take 2 hours, and author's corrections take 5 hours. Camera, stripping, and plating take 9 hours. The press operator uses 2 hours for makeready and 7 hours for running time. The bindery department takes 23 hours to complete the folding and stitching. How many hours of chargeable time are required to do this job? _____

2. A printing department completes the following impressions in 1 day: 1760 tickets, 860 envelopes, 2125 business cards, 1240 invoices, 3600 circulars, and 1200 labels. What is the total number of impressions printed during the day? _____

3. The production manager requests the following kinds of paper be sent to the pressroom: 463 reams of bond, 987 reams of index, 945 reams of coated stock, and 27 reams of text. Determine the total number of reams delivered to the pressroom. _____

4. Job A takes 48 hours to complete, job B takes 19 hours to complete, job C requires 32 hours to complete, and job D requires 15 hours to complete. What is the total number of hours required to complete the 4 jobs? _____

5. On a certain printing job, the following stock is used: 3980 sheets the first day, 3986 sheets the second day, and 4220 sheets the third day. How many sheets of stock are used? _____

6. Employees of a certain printing company include: 33 office workers; 42 phototypesetters; 75 keyliners, camera operators, strippers, and platemakers; 54 press operators; 19 stock cutters; 14 bindery workers; 1 sales manager and 6 sales representatives; and 13 commercial artists. What is the total number of employees? _____

7. A printing concern prints 16,150 tags on Monday, 17,050 tags on Tuesday, 17,500 tags on Wednesday, 18,008 tags on Thursday, and 17,364 tags on Friday. The following week, 4000 more tags than the number printed the preceding week are printed. How many tags are printed in the 2 weeks?

_____

8. Four different printing jobs are billed out as follows: $329, $645, $893, and $275. What is the total revenue from these jobs?

_____

9. Publication A contains 10,934 ems of type; publication B contains 12,894 ems; publication C has 13,697 ems; publication D has 14,302 ems; and publication E has 21,789 ems. What is the total number of ems of type set in these publications?

_____

10. Three large printing firms employ the following number of people: firm A, 465; firm B, 238; and firm C, 197. Determine the total number of people employed by these 3 firms.

_____

11. During a 5-month period, a monthly magazine prints the following number of copies: 150,000; 154,598; 162,347; 158,994; and 168,203. What is the total number of copies printed in the 5-month period?

_____

12. The number of ems of type in the first job is 33,040; in the second job, 9305; in the third job, 9565; and in the last job, 4997. What is the total number of ems in the 4 jobs?

_____

13. A press operator prints 13,540 letterheads on Monday; 15,794 letterheads on Tuesday; 18,947 letterheads on Wednesday; and 9823 letterheads on Thursday. How many letterheads are printed during the 4-day period?

_____

14. Determine the total amount of a weekly payroll that is made up as follows:

    3 Phototypesetters $1050
    2 Press Operators . . . . $ 840
    1 Paste-up Artist . . . . $ 340
    1 Bindery Machine Operator . . . . . . $ 370
    1 Proofreader . . . . $ 318

_____

15. Determine the number of books delivered on a certain order if they are sent out in 4 lots as follows: 10,525 on Monday; 7850 on Tuesday; 14,800 on Wednesday; 0 on Thursday, and 16,575 on Friday.

_____

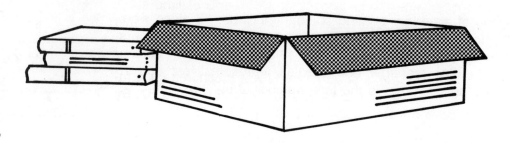

Unit 2   SUBTRACTION OF WHOLE NUMBERS

BASIC PRINCIPLES

- Apply the principles of subtraction to the printing and graphic communications industry by solving the practical problems in this unit.

PRACTICAL PROBLEMS

1. If a quantity of paper stock is bought for $43,650 and sold for $45,000, what is the amount of profit?

2. A large printer employs 348 workers. Because of a slump in the economy, 125 workers are laid off. How many workers are still on the payroll after the layoff?

3. If an instant print shop has 27,000 sheets (54 reams) of bond paper in stock and uses 12,500 sheets, how many sheets of bond paper are left?

4. On a certain job, John runs 52,598 sheets of stock. On a similar job, Mary runs 52,308 sheets of stock. How many more sheets does John run than Mary?

5. Phototypesetter A sets 12,023 ems of type and phototypesetter B sets 5,645 ems of type. How many more ems of type does phototypesetter A set than phototypesetter B?

6. The estimated value of a printing shop is $137,500. Since the appraisal, the shop has depreciated $2500. What is the present value of the shop?

7. Folder operator A produces 46,200 signatures during the day shift, and folder operator B runs 26,900 signatures during the night shift. Folder operator A produces how many more signatures than folder operator B?

8. The records at inventory time show that 127 reams of litho stock are on hand. When an actual count is taken, 119 reams of this stock are on hand. The records are in error by how many reams?

9. Two printing firms submit bids on a quantity of brochures for a famous fishing resort. Printer A bids $5239. Printer B bids $5457. By what amount does printer B lose the bid?

10. A certain job has a total of 78,400 ems of type. The phototypesetter sets 40,280 ems the first day. How many ems need to be set the second day to complete the job?

_____

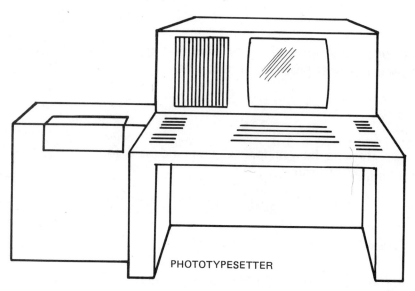

PHOTOTYPESETTER

11. During January, ABC Litho Press completes 623 jobs. In January of the previous year, they completed 591 jobs. How many more jobs did ABC Litho Press complete this January than last January?

_____

12. A press operator has a run of 32,000 impressions to print. Due to mechanical problems, the press operator completes only 10,789 impressions the first day. How many impressions need to be run on the second day to complete the job?

_____

13. A phototypesetter sets 11,854 ems of 6-point type on the first job. On the second job, the phototypesetter sets 14,332 ems of 8-point type. How many more ems are set on the second job than on the first job?

_____

14. A printer has assets valued at $164,250, of which $37,500 is invested in bank stock, $27,460 is invested in mortgages, and the remaining amount is invested in the printing business. How much has the printer invested in the printing business?

_____

15. Feeders (bindery workers) work 37 hours during a normal workweek. Job A takes 7 hours to complete, job B takes 6 hours to complete, and job C requires the rest of the workweek to complete. How many hours are required to complete job C?

_____

Unit 3 MULTIPLICATION OF WHOLE NUMBERS

BASIC PRINCIPLES

- Apply the principles of multiplication to the printing and graphic communications industry by solving the practical problems in this unit.

PRACTICAL PROBLEMS

1. A printer purchases 6 reams of 8 1/2″ × 11″, 20-pound bond stock. At broken carton prices, it sells for $14 per ream. How much is paid for this order? _____

2. If a ream contains 500 sheets, how many sheets of paper are there in 15 reams? _____

3. The average daily production per hour for a group of 4, 19″ × 25″ stream-fed offset presses is 7000 on each press. What is the average daily production if a workday is 8 hours long? _____

4. If a press operator runs the press at 5250 impressions in an average hour of production, how many impressions can be printed in 4 days? (There are 8 hours in 1 day.) _____

5. On a daily newspaper, the keyboard operator sets an average of 273 lines per hour of display type for ads. How many lines are set in a 40-hour week? _____

6. A certain printing job requires 47 hours of labor to complete. The labor rate per hour is $11. How much labor is charged to this printing job? _____

7. An estimator determines that a printing job requires 346 reams of stock. The cost for this stock is $25 per ream. What is the cost of the stock for this printing job? _____

8. To run a catalog, 47 plates are required. The cost for each plate is $2. What is the total cost for the plates? _____

9. Eight letterheads are printed at the same time on a 23″ × 35″ sheet. The press operator runs 3750 impressions. How many letterheads are produced from this press run? _____

10. If a ream of 17″ × 22″ stock weighs 24 pounds, what is the weight of 34 reams? _____

11. A page of 8-point type contains 1620 ems of type. How many ems of type are contained in 168 pages of 8-point type? _____

12. A 2 volume dictionary has 1980 pages of 8-point type. Each page contains 4130 ems of type. How many ems of type are contained in the 2 volumes? _____

13. It is possible to cut 110, 2″ × 3 1/2″ cards from a sheet of plate stock. How many cards can be cut from 3468 sheets of stock? _____

14. A stripper can strip a 1-color page in 3 minutes. How long does it take to strip a 64-page, 1-color magazine? _____

15. The hourly cost for producing halftones on a 20″ × 24″ camera is $31. How much cost is charged to a job if it takes 3 hours to produce the halftones? _____

Unit 4 DIVISION OF WHOLE NUMBERS

BASIC PRINCIPLES

- Apply the principles of division to the printing and graphic communications industry by solving the practical problems in this unit.

PRACTICAL PROBLEMS

1. From a sheet of 22″ × 34″ stock, 8 letterheads are obtained. How many sheets of 22″ × 34″ are needed to obtain 15000 letterheads? _____

2. A certain job requires that 42,250 copies be folded by 5 workers. What is the average number of copies folded by each worker? _____

3. Determine the number of reams (500 sheets per ream) in a lot of 458,500 sheets. _____

4. It is possible to purchase 25 reams of 25″ × 38″ coated book stock for $775. What is the cost per ream? _____

5. A certain printing firm employs 23 people. Their union negotiates a health-care package that amounts to $13,754. To what extent does each employee benefit? _____

6. A duplicator is purchased by a job-shop proprietor for $16,470 (including interest). Equal monthly payments are to be made over a 27-month period. What is the amount payable each month? _____

7. How many circulars can be printed in 1 hour if the average daily output (7-hour shift) is 29,925 impressions? _____

8. A booklet contains 2360 lines of 10-point type. If there are 40 lines on each page, find the number of pages in the booklet. _____

9. In a month, a printer specializing in printing business cards sells 369 orders for a total of $4059. What is the average cost for each order? _____

10. An estimate is prepared for a customer's catalog. It is determined that 42 large metal plates are needed to complete the job. The total cost for the large metal plates is $378. What is the cost for each plate? _____

11. A paper cutter operator cuts 4 equal lengths from a sheet measuring 36 inches. What is the length of each piece? _____

12. The payroll of a printing shop includes the following information for a 5-day week (40 hours). What is the hourly wage rate for each person?

    > 3 Phototypesetters $1080
    >
    > 1 Press Operator . . . . $ 400
    >
    > 1 Keyliner $280
    >
    > 1 Bindery Feeder . . . . $ 360
    >
    > 1 Proofreader . . . . $ 320

    _____

13. A lot of 10,000 pamphlets will be mailed. The total weight, before wrapping into bundles, is 40,000 ounces. What is the weight of each pamphlet?

    _____

14. A phototypesetter sets an average of 2070 ems per hour. How much time does it take this phototypesetter to set a job that contains 76,590 ems?

    _____

15. If a ream of paper costs $8, how many reams of paper can be bought for $328?

    _____

Unit 5 ROMAN NUMERALS

BASIC PRINCIPLES

- Apply the principles of Roman numerals to the printing and graphic communications industry by solving the practical problems in this unit.

A printer should be familiar with Roman numerals. Roman numerals are often used on title pages and for chapter headings, or to specify a volume number. Paper dealers also use the Roman numerals C, D, and M after weight or unit cost of paper stock to indicate the weight or cost per 100, 500, or 1000 sheets.

Roman Numerals

The following letters are used to construct the Roman system of enumeration:

letter I = 1
letter V = 5
letter X = 10
letter L = 50

letter C = 100
letter D = 500
letter M = 1000

Expressing Arabic Numerals as Roman Numerals and Vice Versa

The Roman system of enumeration basically uses the principles of addition. When addition is used, this means that separate letters are added, starting with the largest number first, to determine the Arabic number.

The subtractive principle also is used in six specific instances. When subtraction is used, a smaller symbol is placed before a larger symbol. This indicates that the smaller number is subtracted from the larger number. The following are the six instances:

IV = 5 − 1 = 4
XL = 50 − 10 = 40
CD = 500 − 100 = 400

IX = 10 − 1 = 9
XC = 100 − 10 = 90
CM = 1000 − 100 = 900

Examples

1. 55 = 50 + 5 = L + V = LV
2. 1944 = 1000 + 900 + 40 + 4 = M + CM + XL + IV = MCMXLIV
3. CLV = C + L + V = 100 + 50 + 5 = 155
4. CDXXIV = CD + X + X + IV = 500 − 100 + 10 + 10 + 4 = 424

Special Cases

A bar placed over a letter multiplies its value by 1000. For example, $\overline{L}$ = 50,000; $\overline{XX}$ = 20,000.

Lowercase Roman numerals are sometimes used to number introductory pages. For example, page 8 of the introductory pages may be written as viii.

PRACTICAL PROBLEMS

A.   Write the following as Roman numerals.

1. 19 _____   6.   112 _____

2. 14 _____   7.   549 _____

3. 25 _____   8.   494 _____

4. 69 _____   9.   2494 _____

5. 96 _____   10. 1979 _____

B.   Write the following Roman numerals as Arabic numerals.

1. XX _____   6. DCXLVII _____

2. XII _____   7. DIV _____

3. CCCV _____   8. MMCLIX _____

4. CVIII _____   9. CMXCIX _____

5. MCCCL _____   10. DCCXCVIII _____

C.   Write the following as Roman numerals.

1. 6000 _____   3. 75,542 _____

2. 53,647 _____   4. 653,947 _____

D.   Write the following as Arabic numerals.

1. vii _____   4. $\overline{\text{LX}}$ _____

2. iii _____   5. $\overline{\text{CXXX}}$ _____

3. xvi _____   6. $\overline{\text{CXLVII}}$CXXII _____

Unit 6 ADDITION OF FRACTIONS

BASIC PRINCIPLES

- Apply the principles of addition of fractions to the printing and graphic communications industry by solving the practical problems in this unit.

PRACTICAL PROBLEMS

1. A certain job ticket has the following times recorded: artwork, 2 1/2 hours; composition, 1 1/2 hours; camera, 1/2 hour; stripping, 1/2 hour; prepress color proofing, 1 1/2 hours. What is the total time recorded on this job ticket? _____

2. A pressroom lead person orders ink in the following quantities: warm red, 5 1/4 pounds; fast-dry black, 10 3/4 pounds; process blue, 7 5/8 pounds; magenta, 2 1/2 pounds. How many pounds of ink are ordered altogether? _____

3. An estimator figures paper for the following jobs. Job A will take 21 1/2 reams of 25″ × 38″ offset stock; job B will take 12 3/8 reams of 17″ × 22″ no. 4 sulfite; and job C will require 7 3/16 reams of 17 1/2″ × 22 1/2″ 25% rag stock. What is the total number of reams required for the 3 jobs? _____

4. Part of a certain job calls for tabular matter with the following column widths: column 1, 5 1/4 picas; column 2, 3 1/2 picas; column 3, 4 3/4 picas; column 4, 8 picas; and column 5, 5 1/2 picas. What is the total number of picas for the 5 column widths? _____

CATALOG NUMBER	COLOR	ITEM	DESCRIPTION	PRICE
AN 321	RED	201	SOLID STATE	$29.95 EA
AN 322	WHITE	202	SOLID STATE	$29.95 EA
AN 323	BL...	203	...D STATE	$2...
AN 32...		...4		

5. A stripper is asked to strip a 5 1/2" × 8 1/2" book that will be perfect bound. The book will be stripped 8 pages up. The stripper rules out the following dimensions on the flat: 1/8 inch, 5 1/2 inches, 1/8 inch, 1/8 inch, 5 1/2 inches, 1/8 inch, 1/8 inch, 5 1/2 inches, 1/8 inch, 1/8 inch, 5 1/2 inches, and 1/8 inch. What is the total width of sheet needed for this job?

_____

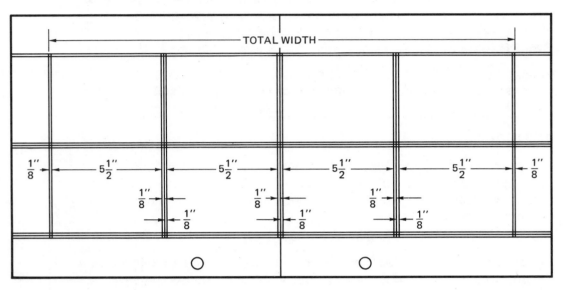

6. This same job (referred to in problem 5) calls for a bleed to be printed on one of the pages next to the gripper. The stripper rules out the following dimensions: 3/8 inch, 1/8 inch, 8 1/2 inches, 1/8 inch, 1/8 inch, 8 1/2 inches, and 1/8 inch. What is the total depth of sheet needed for this job?

_____

7. For a more economical run, several jobs are ganged together. The widths of the 4 jobs are as follows: job A is 3 1/8 inches, job B is 4 3/16 inches, job C is 7 13/16 inches, and job D is 10 3/8 inches. What is the total width of the 4 jobs?

_____

8. To receive freight prepaid on a quantity of paper from the paper house, a printer must order 500 pounds or more. A printer places an order for 127 1/2 pounds of ledger, 60 1/4 pounds of no. 4 sulfite, 75 3/4 pounds of cover, 220 3/8 pounds of index, and 123 7/8 pounds of 10-point board. Find the total number of pounds ordered to see if the printer receives the shipment of paper prepaid.

_____

9. In the press department, 3 different shifts of employees are working the same job. The first shift works 6 1/4 hours, the second shift works 7 1/8 hours, and the third shift works 5 3/8 hours. What is the total number of hours spent on the job by the 3 shifts?

_____

10. During the week, the camera department works on several jobs. Their productive time is recorded as follows: Monday, 6 3/10 hours; Tuesday, 7 5/10 hours; Wednesday, 6 4/10 hours; Thursday, 5 9/10 hours; and Friday, 7 1/10 hours. What is the total number of hours of productive time during the week? _____

11. In preparing a mechanical for a 2-page layout, an artist measures the following dimensions: left margin, 5/8 inch; type area, 4 3/4 inches; gutter, 1 1/4 inches; photo, 2 1/2 inches; white space, 1/8 inch; type area, 2 1/8 inches; and right margin, 5/8 inch. What is the total width of the 2-page layout? _____

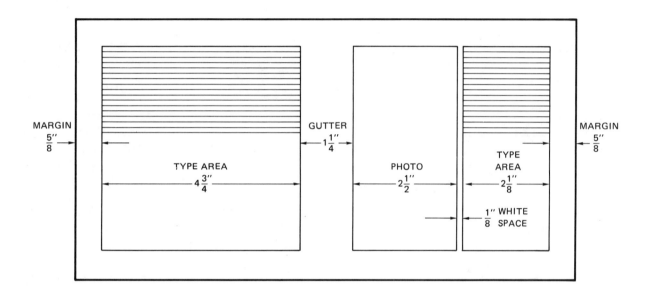

12. A periodic inventory of the cases of envelopes reveals the following information: 4 1/2 cases of 6 3/4-size envelopes, 7 3/4 cases of no. 10's, 2 1/4 cases of no. 10 windows, 1 3/4 cases of no. 9's, and 3 1/4 cases of ivory colored A-2's. What is the total number of cases of envelopes in inventory? _____

13. A sales representative records the following times on a call sheet: travel, 1/2 hour; customer A, 1 1/4 hours; travel, 1/4 hour; lunch with customer B, 1 3/8 hours; travel, 3/4 hour; customer C, 1/4 hour; and travel, 3/4 hour. What is the total time recorded on the call sheet by the sales representative? _____

14. The layout of a newspaper page is being planned. The editor decides on a 5-column format for the page. Each column is to be 2 1/8 inches wide, the distance between each column is to be 1/8 inch, and each margin is to be 3/4 inch. What is the total width of the page?

   _____

15. A 3-column ad is to appear in the same paper referred to in problem 14. The editor uses the same column measurements as in problem 14. What is the total width of this ad?

   _____

Unit 7 SUBTRACTION OF FRACTIONS

BASIC PRINCIPLES

- Apply the principles of subtraction of fractions to the printing and graphic communications industry by solving the practical problems in this unit.

PRACTICAL PROBLEMS

1. A job is set by Jim, a journeyman phototypesetter, in 7 3/4 fewer hours than it takes Linda, an apprentice phototypesetter. Linda takes 10 1/4 hours to set the job. How long did it take Jim to set the job? _____

2. A job is set 7 1/2 inches (45 picas) wide and printed on a sheet 9 1/4 inches wide with a 3/4-inch margin on the left-hand side. How much space remains for the right-hand margin? _____

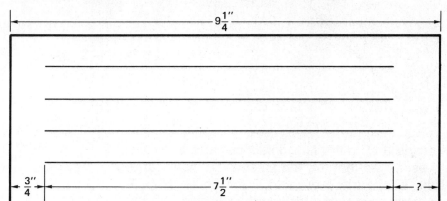

3. A printer has 8 3/4 reams of book paper in stock. The printer uses 1/3 of a ream on a short run. How many reams remain? _____

4. A press operator receives 7 5/8 pounds of process blue ink from the stockroom. On Monday, the operator uses 2 3/4 pounds of the ink. How much ink remains? _____

5. When the regular monthly inventory is conducted, the person counting finds 27 3/4 reams. The inventory record indicates that there are 28 1/2 reams. How much in error is the inventory record? _____

6. The estimating department figures that a certain 2-color brochure job will take 17 3/10 hours to complete. When the time sheet arrived back in the office, the actual time spent on the job was 15 6/10 hours. How many fewer hours did it take the press department to do the job than was estimated? _____

7. A brochure design is being worked on by the art department. The customer wants it to fit into a no. 10 envelope, which measures 4 1/8 inches on one side. Because of its bulkiness, the brochure must be 1/4 inch less than the envelope. What width should the finished brochure be?

_____

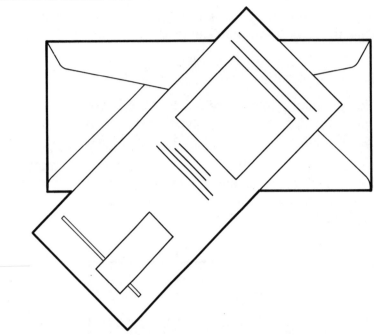

8. A printing firm sends 3 of their plant personnel to a seminar in a distant city. It is estimated that the trip takes 3 1/4 hours to drive. The traffic is light, so the trip only takes 2 3/4 hours. How much time is saved on their drive to the distant city?

_____

9. A cutter operator cuts a 23" (width) × 35" (length) sheet of stock into the following lengths: 8 1/2 inches, 8 1/4 inches, 8 5/8 inches. What is the length of paper that remains?

_____

10. A total of 14 9/10 hours are needed to complete a press run. The day shift starts the job and records 7 1/2 hours on their time sheet. How much time remains for the next 2 shifts to complete the job?

_____

11. The prepress proofs must be mailed within 6 3/10 hours. The camera department needs 3 6/10 hours to shoot the negatives. How much time remains for the stripping and proofing of this job?

_____

12. Because of machinery breakdowns, a job that normally takes 36 3/4 hours actually takes 42 7/10 hours. By what amount of time does the printer miss the deadline?

13. Inventory control is an important factor in any business. The inventory records indicate that there are 27 3/4 pounds of black ink on hand. An apprentice locates only 24 7/16 pounds. How many pounds short is the supply of black ink?

14. A customer arrives at an instant print shop promptly at 8:00 AM. The customer needs 3 reports for a 2:30 PM meeting that same day (6 1/2 hours later). The press department needs 3/4 of an hour for the first report, and 1 1/4 and 1 1/2 hours respectively for the second and third reports. The bindery department needs 2 hours to complete stapling of the reports. By what margin of time does the shop expect to complete the job?

15. A stripper is required to gang up several jobs on a press run. Job A is 6 1/4 inches wide, job B is 8 3/4 inches wide, and job C is 6 15/16 inches wide. The paper stock cut for the press is 23 inches wide. How much trim is left?

Unit 8 MULTIPLICATION OF FRACTIONS

BASIC PRINCIPLES

• Apply the principles of multiplication of fractions to the printing and graphic communications industry by solving the practical problems in this unit.

PRACTICAL PROBLEMS

1. A camera operator works 3 1/2 days on a printing job. If there are 7 1/2 hours in a workday, how many hours are charged to this job? _____

2. A press operator estimates that 4 1/2 hours are required to run a certain job. The operator averages 6700 impressions each hour. What is the total number of impressions printed for this job? _____

3. A page contains 25 lines of type. Each line occupies 2 1/3 picas. What is the total depth of the page in picas? _____

4. The type selected for a manuscript averages 15 1/2 words per set line. The manuscript yields 240 lines of type. How many words are contained in the manuscript? _____

5. To meet a deadline and to increase profit, the manager of a printing shop often gangs jobs on the larger presses. Four jobs, each measuring 8 3/4 inches wide, are run on 1 sheet. The scrap is 3 inches. How wide is the press sheet? (There is no trim between the 4 jobs.) _____

6. A press department employs 4 press operators who work 7 1/2 hours each day. Their workweek consists of 5 1/2 days. What is the total number of hours the press department works in a week. _____

7. A page of type consists of 5 columns, each 2 3/16 inches wide. Each column is separated by 1/8 inch, and both the right and left margins are 3/4 inch wide. How many inches wide is this page of type? _____

8. Five tickets are run up on a sheet. Each ticket measures 2 1/8 inches deep. How long is the sheet? (Remember to add a 3/8-inch gripper margin.) _____

9. A case-bound book weighs 1 1/4 pounds. What is the total weight of 1570 case-bound books? _____

10. Each signature of a magazine uses 2 3/8 rolls of paper. The magazine contains 5 signatures. How many rolls of paper are used for this magazine? _____

11. A press run is consuming an average of 3 7/16 pounds of black ink per hour. The press is run for 6 7/10 hours on a certain job. How many pounds of black ink are used? _____

12. A line of 10-point type contains an average of 11 1/2 words. How many words are contained in 175 lines of type? _____

13. To complete the collating and stitching of a large wholesale catalog requires 3 shifts working 7 1/2 hours per shift for 4 days. What is the total number of hours charged to this job? _____

14. A worker puts in 9 3/10 hours per day for 5 days. How many hours are recorded on the worker's time card? _____

15. A ream of paper weighs 20 1/2 pounds. What is the weight of a skid containing 40 1/2 reams? _____

Unit 9 DIVISION OF FRACTIONS

BASIC PRINCIPLES

- Apply the principles of division of fractions to the printing and graphic communications industry by solving the practical problems in this unit.

PRACTICAL PROBLEMS

1. A phototypesetter completes a manuscript containing 7650 characters in 4 1/4 hours. How many characters are typeset per hour? _____

2. A line of type measures 25 picas long and contains 62 1/2 characters. What is the number of characters per pica? _____

3. A press operator produces 69,375 impressions during 7 1/2 hours of productive time. On the average, how many impressions are produced per hour? _____

4. A paper house is clearing out some odd-lot stock. One skid weighs 750 3/4 pounds. Each ream weights 20 pounds. How many reams of stock are contained on this skid of paper? _____

5. Folders are sometimes rated in inches per hour rather than sheets per hour. A certain folding machine and operator logs 106,562 1/2 inches in 3 7/8 hours. How many inches per hour did the machine run? _____

6. The estimating department figures that the press run for a booklet will take 12 2/10 hours of running time. The run is for 85,000 booklets. How many impressions per hour must the press operator average to stay within the estimated running time? _____

7. A camera operator, using an automatic camera attached to a processor, puts out 152 line negatives during 7 6/10 hours. How many shots are made during the average hour? _____

8. When costing out a job, it is found that the press run takes 22 3/4 pounds of ink. The ink costs $182. What is the cost of the ink per pound? _____

9. Book paper comes in sheets that measure 25″ × 38″. A job to be cut from this stock requires a sheet that measures 9 1/2″ × 12 1/2.″ How many 9 1/2-inch sheets can be cut from the 38-inch length? _____

10. Using the same information given in question 9, how many 12 1/2-inch sheets can be cut from the 25-inch measurement? _____

11. A cutter operator cuts a 19″ × 25″ sheet into 3 1/2-inch square sheets. How many 3 1/2-inch lengths does the operator obtain from the 25-inch length of the sheet?   _____

12. A manuscript contains 10,576 words. Each page of type has an average of 210 1/2 words. How many pages are contained in the manuscript?   _____

13. A printer cuts 5″ × 7″ cards from 22 1/2 inches of index stock. How many 5-inch cuts are obtained from the 22 1/2-inch length?   _____

14. A printer usually keeps large sheets of scrap paper on hand. This same printer cuts 4 3/4″ × 9″ pieces from a 29 1/2″ × 9″ sheet of scrap paper. How many small sheets are cut from the large sheet?   _____

15. An operator is asked to set tabular matter on a phototypesetter. The assignment calls for 10 columns to fit equally into 37 1/2 picas. How wide is each column?   _____

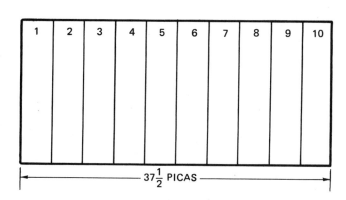

Unit 10 ADDITION OF DECIMALS

BASIC PRINCIPLES

- Apply the principles of addition of decimals to the printing and graphic communications industry by solving the practical problems in this unit.

PRACTICAL PROBLEMS

1. An estimating department figures that it takes the following number of hours to complete a certain job: 3.75 hours, artwork and mechanicals; .50 hour, typesetting; .33 hour, camera department; .74 hour; stripping; .30 hour, platemaking; and 4.60 hours, press and bindery. What is to total number of hours estimated to complete this job? _____

2. Two different presses are working on the same job during a 3-day period. Press A operates for 6.5 hours on Monday, 7.3 hours on Tuesday, and 4.6 hours on Wednesday; Press B runs for 3.7 hours on Monday, 6.8 hours of Tuesday, and 6.9 hours on Wednesday. What is the total number of hours the 2 presses operate during the 3-day period? _____

3. To take advantage of prepaid freight from the paper house, the purchasing agent orders 240.666 pounds of 60-pound vellum, 420.250 pounds of 50-pound uncoated offset, and 400.789 pounds of 20-pound no. 4 sulfite. What is the total weight of the shipment of paper? _____

4. A printing buyer accepts several bids from 4 printers on a variety of jobs. Printer A bids $4789.38 for brochures; printer B bids $2397.45 for statements and envelopes; printer C bids $789.29 for direct-mail flyers; and printer D bids $1807.03 for order books. What is the total printing cost for the 4 orders? _____

5. Monthly expenses for a certain printing company are as follows: salaries and related taxes, $33,789.04; utilities, $2515.89; building rent, $8750.50; insurance, $479.83; repairs, $348.95; and miscellaneous expenses, $74.73. What are the total expenses for the month? _____

6. A keyliner puts the following measurements on the art board for the placement of type and artwork in a job; left margin, .75 inch; text, 3.125 inches; screened print, 2.5 inches; and right margin, .75 inch. What is the total width of this job?

_____

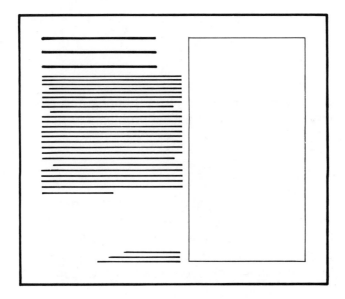

7. In a certain printing firm, the receipts for the first quarter are as follows:

January	$11,289.43
February	12,769.57
March	14,863.69

What are the total receipts?

_____

8. A folder operator's time card shows the following hours are worked: Monday, 8.2 hours, Tuesday, 9.5 hours, Wednesday, 8.6 hours, Thursday, 8.2 hours, and Friday, 7.8 hours. What is the total number of hours worked by the folder operator?

_____

9. The press operator has to repack a blanket. The following thicknesses of packing paper are added: 2 sheets each .057 inch, 1 sheet .040 inch, and 1 sheet .0375 inch. What is the total thickness of the packing added under the blanket?

_____

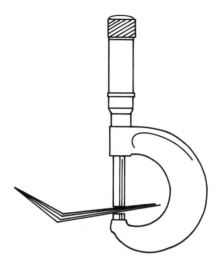

10. A printing job requires 4.2 hours in typesetting, 2.7 hours in keylining, 1.2 hours in camera, 1.7 hours in stripping, and .75 hour in platemaking. How many hours are charged to the job? _____

11. A press operator works the following hours in 1 day: makeready, .75 hour; running time, 4.35 hours; cleanup, .50 hour; and preventative maintenance, 1.9 hours. What is the total number of hours worked in 1 day by the press operator? _____

12. A check on the storeroom reveals the following quantities of ink on hand: cyan, 7.5 pounds; black, 27.3 pounds; brown, 4.8 pounds; green, 5.2 pounds; yellow, 12.4 pounds; magenta, 9.6 pounds; purple, 1.7 pounds; and mixing white, 6.4 pounds. What is the total number of pounds of ink in the storeroom? _____

13. The owner checks the ledger and finds the following accounts are due and payable on the tenth of the month: account A, $786.54; account B, $1245.89; account C, $87.95; and account D, $256.74. What is the total of the 4 accounts due the printer? _____

14. The estimating department bids on the following jobs on Monday: pamphlets, $1278.64; letterheads, $89.04; envelopes, $174.56; 3-part carbonless forms, $1765.89; 4-color envelope stuffers, $10,876.93. What is the total dollar amount bid on Monday? _____

15. Four jobs are to be ganged on a press run. The first job measures 4.25 inches wide, the second job measures 5.5 inches wide, the third job measures 6.75 inches wide, and the fourth job measures 8.5 inches. The total trim for the 4 jobs is 2.3 inches. What is the minimum width of paper that these jobs can be run on? _____

Unit 11   SUBTRACTION OF DECIMALS

BASIC PRINCIPLES

- Apply the principles of subtraction of decimals to the printing and graphic communications industry by solving the practical problems in this unit.

PRACTICAL PROBLEMS

1. The monthly receipts for the ABC Type House amount to $20,834.34, and the expenses are $18,750.91. What is the profit for the month? _____

2. The periodic inventory of the dollar amount of paper stock reveals that there is $4764.29 on hand. Thirty days later, a second inventory reveals a drop to $3975.39. How much less than the first inventory is the dollar amount now? _____

3. Sales figures are often a barometer of how well a printer is doing. The sales last September were $24,786.93. This September, the sales amount to $21,956.47. By what amount are the sales down this September? _____

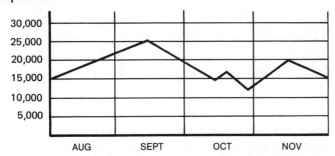

4. Real profit is not always shown in the dollar amount of sales, but in how efficiently the jobs are produced. Last year, 4-part carbonless form was produced on an older press in 21.75 hours. This year, because of the acquisition of a new press, this same job is run in 18.25 hours. How much time is saved by using the new machinery? _____

5. The estimating department of a large litho shop figures that the cost of producing a brochure will be $1345.63. When the job is complete and the figures are gathered, the actual cost is $1298.97. How much under the estimated amount is the job run? _____

6. The press room is scheduled to complete a certain job in 16.7 hours. Because of poor ink drying between runs, the job actually takes 19.3 hours. How much longer than is scheduled does this job take to complete? _____

7. A brochure being printed on a 2-color press is estimated to use 9.5 pounds of black ink and 3.7 pounds of red ink. The run actually uses 10.1 pounds of black ink and 4.2 pounds of red ink. How much more red and black ink does the run actually use than was estimated?

8. An experienced stripper and an apprentice are both working on the same job. The experienced stripper strips 8 pages of color in 3.6 hours, while the apprentice strips 8 pages of color in 6.8 hours. How much faster than the apprentice does the experienced stripper strip 8 pages?

9. Two press operators work for the same company. Press operator A, who frequently works overtime hours, earns $25,585.75 a year. Press operator B earns $22,360.89 a year. How much more than press operator B does press operator A earn a year?

10. When a certain printing company first started in business, it developed its film in the tray. At that time, a job containing 100 sheets of 10″ × 12″ film was processed in 4.69 hours dry to dry. As the firm grew, it purchased an automatic processor. Using this new equipment, the firm now processes 100 sheets of 10″ × 12″ film in 1.90 hours dry to dry. How much time is saved by using the new processor?

11. A job that is bid to be run on a 19″ × 25″ press has a pressroom cost factor of $57.00. Because of a breakdown on this press, the job is run on a smaller press. The pressroom cost factor for the smaller press amounts to $153.99. How much over the estimate does this make the job?

12. Inventory systems usually carry a reorder point for every item that is commonly used in production. For a certain printing company, the normal inventory of black ink is established at 90 pounds. Because of a breakdown in communications, the inventory drops to 19.67 pounds. How many pounds of ink must be ordered to bring the inventory back to normal?

13. Mixing of chemicals is a routine job that every camera operator performs. The formula for the working solution of fixer is: .50 gallon of water, .25 gallon of solution A, and .05 gallon of solution B. In order to complete the mix, the camera operator must bring the combined solution to a full gallon by adding more water. How much more water is needed to make 1 gallon of working solution?

_____

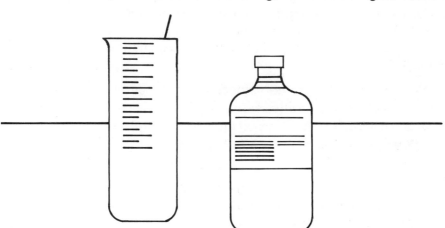

14. To boost sales, a sales manager offers the sales representative with the most sales during a promotion a weekend trip for 2 to a popular resort. Sales representative A has sales that amount to $147,986.47 during the promotion, and sales representative B has sales that amount to $152,797.84 during the same period. By what margin does sales representative B win the trip?

_____

15. A keyliner is preparing a layout for paste-up. The halftone takes 2.25 inches of space, and the copy takes 4.625 inches of space. The sheet to be printed on is 8.5 inches wide. How much white space is left for margins?

_____

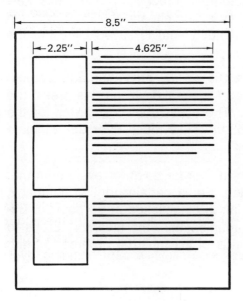

Unit 12 MULTIPLICATION OF DECIMALS

BASIC PRINCIPLES

- Apply the principles of multiplication of decimals to the printing and graphic communications industry by solving the practical problems in this unit.

PRACTICAL PROBLEMS

1. What is the gross weekly pay for a press operator who earns $9.75 per hour and works 37.5 hours? _____

2. The phototype department spends 3.5 hours on a certain job. This department is charged out at the rate of $38.75 per hour. What is the total cost to the customer for this job? _____

3. An inventory reveals that a certain printing company has 47.33 reams of stock on hand. The cost for this stock is $65.89 per ream. What is the total value of this stock? _____

4. A print shop specializing in business cards, sells their product through dealers. On Monday, 497 orders are sold at an average cost of $9.48 per order. What is the amount of sales for Monday? _____

5. A catalog requires 75 line shots on 10″ × 12″ film. The cost of film is $67.98 per 100 sheets of 10″ × 12″ film. What is the total cost of film for the catalog? _____

6. In the press department, 3.7 hours are required to run a 2-color letterhead job. This press is costed out at the rate of $20.65 per hour. What is the charge for press time on this job? _____

7. A tabular form calls for 6 columns, each 1.67 inches wide. What is the total width needed for the tabular form (The space needed between columns should not be considered when figuring this problem.) _____

$1234.70 $ $9654.12 $127.56 $ $

8. An employee in the bindery department earns $8.69 per hour. The regular workweek is 37.5 hours. The employee is paid time and a half for any overtime hours. This week, a certain employee works 43.25 hours. What is the employee's gross pay including overtime? _____

9. A keyboard operator sets an average of 25.5 words per minute. At this rate, how many words can be set in 1.875 hours? _____

10. The average sales per month for the ABC Printing Company is $19,276.43. Based on this average, what is the total yearly sales? _____

11. Based on a press running heavy coverage of black ink, 5.66 pounds of ink are used per hour. The press is run 3.75 hours for this type of coverage. How many pounds of ink are consumed? _____

12. The ABC Printing Company employs 3 full-time sales representatives. The total average daily sales amounts to $4674.89. What is the total amount of sales for a 5.5-day workweek? _____

13. The estimating department furnishes sales representative A with figures for a brochure job. The job is estimated to take 3.6 hours to fold, and the folder is rated at $27.50 per hour. What is the cost for folding this brochure job? _____

14. The inside of a 108-page book is printed on paper that "mikes" out at .0035 inch per sheet. What is the total thickness of the inside of this book? _____

? THICKNESS

15. A camera operator who earns $9.75 per hour works 2.3 hours on a certain printing job. A platemaker who earns $8.60 per hour works 1.7 hours on the same job. Compute the total wages charged to this printing job. _____

Unit 13 DIVISION OF DECIMALS

BASIC PRINCIPLES

- Apply the principles of division of decimals to the printing and graphic communications industry by solving the practical problems in this unit.

PRACTICAL PROBLEMS

1. During an average week, a sales representative for a printing firm has sales that amount to $6500.16. The sales representative works 4.5 days per week. What is the average sales per day? _____

2. On Tuesday, an operator prints 33,750 no. 10 envelopes on a small duplicator during a 7.5-hour shift. How many envelopes are printed in the average hour on Tuesday? _____

3. According to an estimate, a 28,600 single-color run can be completed in 3.25 hours. How many impressions per hour must the press operator maintain to meet the estimate? _____

4. A printer orders 3000 reams of no. 5 sulfite cut 8 1/2″ × 11″. The total cost for the order is $13,125.00. What is the cost per ream? _____

5. The average line of 10-point type contains 68.75 characters. This particular family of 10-point type sets 2.5 characters per pica. How many picas wide is this line of type? _____

6. A printing firm purchases 350 plates for their 19″ × 25″ press. The total bill amounts to $1522.50. What is the cost for each plate? _____

7. The total bill for a printing job amounts to $650.45. The sales department notes that this amount is higher than the original estimate, so they request a breakdown of the bill. The job required 16 pieces of film at a cost of $39.28. What was the cost for each individual piece of film? _____

8. In a further investigation of the same printing job in problem 7, the sales department discovered that the press time cost the customer $78.00, and the time spent on the press was 2 hours and 40 minutes. What was the cost per hour for press time? _____

9. Sales representative A submits a job to the estimating department for a cost figure. The cost for press time is $132.09 for 3.7 hours of running time. What is the cost per hour for this particular press? _____

10. An agency charges a printing firm $75.80 for artwork which takes 1 hour and 40 minutes. What is the rate per hour that this agency charges? _____

11. An inventory of the paper stock reveals that there is a total of 29.20 reams of book paper on hand. The total for the stock amounts to $902.28. What is the cost per ream? _____

12. To give estimates on printing jobs, the estimating department must know unit prices on such items as film and plates. When checking the billing from the supply house, the estimator finds that 10" × 12" line film costs $68.74 per 100 sheets. What is the cost for each individual sheet? _____

13. A 17.5-inch sheet is cut into 10 equal pieces. What is the length of each piece? _____

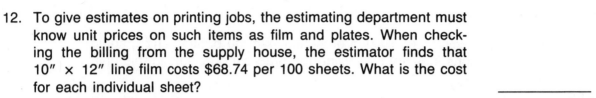

14. A 36-pica line of type is set. The type style and size is Century medium 14 point. Sixty-seven typewritten letters fit into this line. To the nearest thousandth, how many characters per pica are contained in this line of type? _____

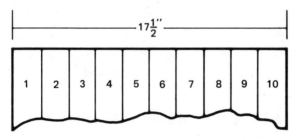

15. In checking the amount of stock on hand, the press department discovers they have 10.4 reams (500 sheets of paper per ream) of the correct stock. The printing job calls for a booklet containing 4 sheets of paper. How many booklets can be printed from this amount of stock? (Overrun for spoilage should not be considered.) _____

Unit 14 PERCENT EQUIVALENTS

BASIC PRINCIPLES

- Apply the principles of percent equivalents to the printing and graphic communications, industry by solving the practical problems in this unit.

Expressing Percents as Decimals

Percent means *per hundred*. To express a percent as a decimal, divide by 100. To divide by 100, simply move the decimal point 2 places to the left.

Examples

1. 3% = .03
2. 63 1/2% = 63.5% = .635

Expressing Percents as Fractions

To express a percent as a fraction, divide by 100. The division should be done as a fractional problem.

Examples

1. 3% = 3 ÷ 100 = 3/1 × 1/100 = 3/100
2. 66 2/3 % = 66 2/3 ÷ 100 = 200/3 × 1/100 = 200/300 = 2/3

Expressing Decimals as Percents

To express a decimal as a percent, multiply by 100. To multiply by 100, simply move the decimal point 2 places to the right.

Examples

1. .75 = 75%
2. .387 = 38.7%

Expressing Fractions as Percents

To express a fraction as a percent, multiply by 100. The multiplication should be done as a fractional problem.

Examples

    1. $3/5 = 3/5 \times 100/1 = 300/5 = 60\%$

    2. $5/6 = 5/6 \times 100/1 = 500/6 = 83 \ 1/3\%$

PRACTICAL PROBLEMS

A. Express the following percents as decimals.

1.	15%	_____	6.	83%	_____
2.	30%	_____	7.	925%	_____
3.	145%	_____	8.	3 1/4%	_____
4.	1/2%	_____	9.	4.81%	_____
5.	8 1/2%	_____	10.	7/8%	_____

B. Express the following percents as fractions.

1.	30%	_____	6.	16 2/3%	_____
2.	60%	_____	7.	33 1/3%	_____
3.	3/4%	_____	8.	475%	_____
4.	56%	_____	9.	12.5%	_____
5.	6 1/4%	_____	10.	87.5%	_____

C. Express the following decimals as percents.

1.	.2	_____	6.	.00875	_____
2.	.45	_____	7.	.65125	_____
3.	.315	_____	8.	2.667	_____
4.	.0037	_____	9.	.001	_____
5.	.625	_____	10.	1.02 3/4	_____

D. Express the following fractions as percents.

1.	2/5	_____	6.	1/8	_____
2.	7/50	_____	7.	1 5/8	_____
3.	1 1/4	_____	8.	18/50	_____
4.	13/20	_____	9.	6 2/5	_____
5.	3/10	_____	10.	9/16	_____

Unit 15 SIMPLE PERCENT

BASIC PRINCIPLES

- Apply the principles of simple percent to the printing and graphic communications industry by solving the practical problems in this unit.

The formula for solving percent problems is $P = B \times R$. R is the rate or the number with the percent sign next to it (e.g., 8%), B is the base or the original quantity, and P is the percentage or the ending amount. A great help in math is to remember that "of" means times $(\times)$ and "is" means equals $(=)$.

PRACTICAL PROBLEMS

1. 45% of 819 =   _____

2. 12 1/2% of 800 =   _____

3. How much is 9% of 164?   _____

4. 5/8% of 600 =   _____

5. What number is 374% of 647?   _____

6. The cost for the stock on the job is $12.90 and the cost of printing the job is $6.75. If the printer figures 20% profit on the stock and 30% profit on the cost of printing, what is the amount of the bill for the job?   _____

7. A printing establishment buys 800 sheets of cover stock. If 15% of this material is damaged by water and 75% of what is left is used on a job, how many sheets are returned to the stock cabinet?   _____

8. A certain paper company has 7439 reams of "1847" bond in their warehouse on January 1. During the month of January, they sell 23% of the stock. In February, they sell 37% of what is on hand the first of the month. What is the amount of stock on hand March 1, if they received a shipment of 5487 reams during February?   _____

9. During a certain year, a printing firm's gross income amounts to $131,500. This income is distributed in the following manner: wages 42%, materials 17%, new equipment and repairs 16%, taxes 2%, interest 3%, reserve 6%, profit 9%, and miscellaneous 5%. How much money is provided for each item   _____

10. 4 is _____% of 40?   _____

11. 5 is what percent of 8?   _____

12. What percent of 48 is 2?   _____

13. 9.6 is what percent of 6.4?   _____

14. What percent of $171 is $135? _____

15. A bill that amounts to $179.65 for letterheads and envelopes is submitted to a customer. In this amount, the printer includes $25 profit. What is the percent of profit for this transaction? _____

16. The estimated time for makeready on a job is 4 1/2 hours. The press operator completes this job in 3 3/4 hours. Find the percent of time gained. _____

17. A loan for a used car is $1575. The interest amounts to $236.25. What is the interest rate for this loan? _____

18. Your pay is raised from $8.20 per hour to $9.20 per hour. What is the percent of increase? _____

19. If the estimated time on a job is 4.2 hours and a compositor takes 5 hours to do the work, what is the compositor's percent of efficiency? _____

20. 44 is 55% of what number? _____

21. 5% of what number is 45? _____

22. 513 is 114% of what number? _____

23. 1/2% of what number is 10? _____

24. 28% of what number is 28? _____

25. A job of printing sells for $1260, which is 12% more than it cost. What does the job cost? _____

26. A printer sells a quantity of paper at a profit of 12 1/2% and gains $250. What is the cost of the paper? _____

27. A firm sells a job of printing that costs $865 at a 15% profit. Another job that costs $1210 sells at an 8% loss. Find the selling price of each job. _____

28. A dealer sells an article for $1.25, thereby making a 25% profit. How much does the article cost the dealer? _____

29. A printer sells a job of printing for $285. If 8% is lost on the job, what does the job cost? _____

30. The materials cost of a job is $636. The printer wants to make a profit of 33 1/3% plus 1/3 of the labor cost. Labor cost is $120.

    (a) What is the profit on the labor? _____

    (b) What is the charge to the customer in order to make the desired profit? _____

31. A bill that amounts to $980.50 for materials is submitted to a customer. Of this amount, 12% is charged for profit. What does the profit amount to? _____

32. A job sells for $17.50. If there is a loss of 8%, what does the job cost?   _____

33. A printer receives an increase of $24.60 per week. This is an increase of 10%. What is the new salary?   _____

34. A house costs $76,500 and grading costs $850. Grading is what percent of the house cost?   _____

35. A new car costs $6255. A down payment of 20% is made, and the balance is paid in 36 monthly installments. How much is paid each month?   _____

36. Your income is $250 per week. Each week you deposit $45 in your savings account. What percent of your income is saved?   _____

Unit 16   INTEREST

BASIC PRINCIPLES

- Apply the principles of interest to the printing and graphic communications industry by solving the practical problems in this unit.

Calculating Interest

Interest is the amount of money paid for the use of borrowed money. Interest is charged as a percent of the amount borrowed. The interest rate is given for 1 year, often called *per annum*. The money may be borrowed for more or less than 1 year. The *principal* is the amount of money borrowed. The following is the formula for calculating interest:

I = P × R × T

Interest = Principal × Rate (in either decimal or fraction form) × Time (in years)

For purposes of this unit, 12 months = 1 year and 365 days = 1 year.

Examples

1. Find the interest on $5280 at 10 1/2% for 3 years.

   I = P × R × T
   I = $5280 × .105 × 3
   I = $1663.20

2. Find the interest on $6475 at 9 3/4% for 11 months.

   I = P × R × T
   I = $6475 × .0975 × 11/12
   I = $578.70

PRACTICAL PROBLEMS

1. A compositor deposits $1245 in a savings bank. If the annual interest rate is 5 1/2%, how much interest is received at the end of the first year?

   _____

2. In order to purchase needed equipment, a printer borrows $785 which is repaid at the end of 9 months. If the interest rate is 15% per annum, find the amount of interest paid by the printer.

   _____

3. Interest on capital investment should be charged by every printer as an item cost of doing business. A certain printer's press equipment is listed at $14,460, composing room equipment is listed at $6040, and bindery equipment is listed at $1242. What is the interest charge for a year if the rate is 16%?

   _____

4. A linotype operator purchases a used car for $1865. After a $350 down payment, a chattel mortgage is given for the remainder of what was agreed to be paid off with interest in 18 months. The total interest charge is $363.60. What is the average interest rate for the time of the loan?

   _____

5. A printer's home is mortgaged for $56,000. In addition to interest at the rate of 17% per annum, the printer agrees to reduce the mortgage $500 every 6 months.

   (a) What is the amount of interest at the end of the first 6 months?

   _____

   (b) What is the amount of interest due at the end of the second 6 months?

   _____

6. The net income of a printing firm for 1 year amounts to $5128. The firm usually figures on approximately 17% net return on their capital investment. The capital investment is as follows: press equipment, $16,375; composing equipment, $7674; bindery equipment $1385; all other investments, $6465. What percent return does the firm receive in this particular year?

   _____

7. A printer deposits $500 in a savings bank on January 1. On July 1, an additional $500 is deposited. The interest rate is 5 1/2% compounded semiannually. This means that the interest accrued in the first 6-month period is added to the principal and draws interest for the next period, and so on. Keeping this in mind, how much is in the printer's bank account 1 year after the first deposit?

   _____

8. Interest in savings banks usually starts the first of each month. A woman deposits $50 each month for 6 months. The interest for the 6-month period is $8.75. What annual rate of interest does this represent for the period?

   _____

9. The cost of a new trimmer is $3495. A printer borrows $4000 at 15 1/2% per annum and repays the loan after 9 months. The trimmer is sold for $4050. How much is gained or lost on the transaction?

   _____

10. To purchase stock in a printing company, a man pays $800 each for 2 shares. The market value of the stock is $1250 for each share at the purchase time. The man is advised that income tax must be paid on the difference between the purchase price and market value. If the tax is computed at 22%, how much tax must the man pay?

   _____

Unit 17 DISCOUNTS

BASIC PRINCIPLES

- Apply the principles of calculating discounts to the printing and graphic communications industry by solving the practical problems in this unit.

Calculating Successive Discounts

Example

Determine the price paid for $365.00 of ink if discounts of 20% and 2% are given.

$ 365.00	Original price
× .20	Discount rate
$ 73.00	1st discount

$ 365.00	Original price
− 73.00	1st discount
$ 292.00	Discounted price
× .02	Discount rate
$ 5.84	2nd discount

$ 292.00	Discounted price
− 5.84	2nd discount
$ 286.16	Price paid

PRACTICAL PROBLEMS

1. A customer purchases the following items: 5000 letterheads at $5.85 per 1000; 5000 envelopes at $4.25 per 1000; and 2500 circulars for which the customer is billed $18.50. If a 2% discount is allowed for cash in 30 days, what will this customer save on the January billing? _____

2. What is the net amount of a printing bill of $60.80 if the discounts are 30% and 10%? _____

3. On a bill of printing amounting to $320, what is the difference in value between a direct discount of 35% and successive discounts of 20% and 15%? _____

4. A printer purchases a ton of linotype metal from a certain foundry at 31 3/4¢ per pound less 10%. The shipping cost is 75¢ per 100 pounds. What is the total cost of the metal delivered? _____

40

5. A printer finds that the cost of production on a certain job is $176.14.

   (a) What is the customer billed if 20% is allowed for profit? _____

   (b) What does the customer pay if 3% cash discount is allowed by this printer? _____

6. A compositor purchases $1450 worth of home furnishings for a new home. This amount is the budget price payable in 24 months. The cash price is 12 1/2% less. The compositor decides to pay cash but requests and receives an additional 2% discount. What amount is paid? _____

7. A printer purchases a quantity of ink that is priced at $189. A direct discount of 32 1/2% is allowed, and if the bill is paid within 30 days, a cash discount of 2% is allowed. What is the net bill? _____

8. A customer is allowed a regular discount of 25% and an additional discount of 2 1/2% for paying cash within 30 days. If the amount of the bill is $435.73, how much does the customer pay assuming the account is settled within the 30 days? _____

9. The stock and labor cost for an order of letterheads and envelopes amounts to $135.64. The printer adds 18% for profit and overhead. Of the total, 54% is allocated to the letterheads and 46% is allocated to the envelopes. What is the total cost for the letterheads and for the envelopes? _____

10. An invoice for $1500 due in 30 days has a 2% cash discount. How much is saved by the printer if $1500 is borrowed for 30 days at 10% and the invoice is paid in cash? _____

Unit 18   RATIO AND PROPORTION

BASIC PRINCIPLES

- Apply the principles of ratio and proportion to the printing and graphic communications industry by solving the practical problems in this unit.

Ratio

A *ratio* is the relationship between 2 quantities of the same kind. A ratio can be expressed in 4 ways: 1) the ratio of 12 to 4; 2) by use of a colon, 12:4; 3) by use of a division sign, $12 \div 4$; or 4) as a fraction, 12/4.

The fractional method is perhaps the easiest form to work with. A ratio is always expressed in lowest terms.

Examples

1. 8/12 = 2/3

2. 10 to 15 = 2 to 3

3. 8:4 = 2:1

4. The ratio of the father's weight to the son's weight is 180 to 75 = 180/75 = 36/15 = 12/5

5. The ratio of the son's weight to the father's weight is 75 to 180 = 5 to 12. (It does matter which number comes first. Keep in mind what is being compared to what.)

6. In order to find the ratio of the father's height to the son's height, it is necessary to express both heights in the same unit. Either 72 inches to 52 inches = 18 to 13 or, 6 feet to 4 1/3 feet = $6 \div 4\ 1/3 = 6/1 \times 3/13 = 18/13$

Percent as a Ratio

Percent is an application of a ratio.

Examples

1. 6% means 6 to 100 = 6/100 = 3/50

2. 5% means 5 to 100 = 5/100 = 1/20

3. 53% means 53 to 100 = 53/100

4. 3 1/3% means 3 1/3 to 100 = $3\ 1/3 \div 100 = 10/3 \times 1/100 = 1/3 \times 1/10 = 1/30$

Proportion

A *proportion* is the equality of 2 (or more) ratios. A proportion can be expressed in 3 ways: 1) 3:4::9:12; 2) 3:4 = 9:12; and 3) 3/4 = 9/12

In each case, the expression is read: 3 is to 4 as 9 is to 12. This text uses the fractional or third form to solve problems. To solve a proportion, cross multiply and then solve for the unknown factor.

Examples

    1. $3/7 = N/14$

        $N = (3 \times 14) \div 7$
        $N = 42 \div 7$
        $N = 6$

    2. $N/6 = 5/3$

        $N = (5 \times 6) \div 3$
        $N = 30 \div 3$
        $N = 10$

    3. $5/8 = 6/N$

        $N = (8 \times 6) \div 5$
        $N = 48 \div 5$
        $N = 9 \, 3/5$

    4. $2\frac{1}{2}/N = 7/6$

        $N = (2\frac{1}{2} \times 6) \div 7$
        $N = 15 \div 7$
        $N = 2 \, 1/7$

PRACTICAL PROBLEMS

A. **Problems 1-10.** Express the following ratios in lowest terms.

    1.   4 to 16   _____   6. 5:2½   _____

    2.   6 to 9   _____   7. .25:.635   _____

    3.   15 to 5   _____   8. 3 inches:1 foot   _____

    4.   32 to 20   _____   9. 52 minutes to 2 hours   _____

    5.   2½:10   _____   10. 45¢ to $5   _____

Problems 11-14. Express the following percents as ratios in lowest terms.

    11. 75% _____   12. 4% _____   13. 2 1/2% _____   14. 115% _____

Problems 15-16. Solve the following problems.

15. A printer earns $275 per week and the printer's assistant earns $150 per week. What is the ratio of the assistant's salary to the printer's salary?   _____

16. The dimensions of a picture are 5″ × 7″. A photographer wants to enlarge it to an 8″ × 10″. What is the ratio of the width of the picture to the width of the enlargement?   _____

B. Solve for N.

1. $N/5 = 7/10$ _____   6. $N/6.3 = 5/8$ _____

2. $8/9 = N/15$ _____   7. $6/N = 10/5$ _____

3. $7/N = 5/6\frac{1}{2}$ _____   8. $N/2\frac{1}{2} = 3/5.7$ _____

4. $3\frac{3}{4}/7 = 5/N$ _____   9. $6\frac{2}{3}/7 = 5/N$ _____

5. $3.4/8 = N/7$ _____   10. $5\frac{1}{3}/6.3 = 8\frac{1}{4}/N$ _____

C. Solve each of the following problems.

1. If a photo measures 6″ × 8″, what size cut should be ordered to fit a space in a newspaper column 12 picas wide?   _____

2. A photo 8″ × 4″ is made into a cut 24 picas wide. What is the depth of cut?   _____

3. A photo 5″ × 6″ is made into a cut for the editorial page of a newspaper. The editorial column is 18 picas wide. How deep is the cut?   _____

4. Copy that is set in a space 18 × 24 picas is to be reset to fit a type page set 36 picas wide. What is the other dimension?   _____

5. A customer calls for a certain shade of yellow ink to be used on a job. From past experience, the press operator determines that 3 3/4 ounces yellow, 1/4 ounce green, and 12 ounces white are needed to make 1 pound of ink the shade the customer desires. The press operator also estimates that to run this particular job requires 3 1/2 pounds of ink. How many ounces of each of the colors are required to make 3 1/2 pounds?   _____

6. In order to match a blue ink, the press operator uses the following formula: 6 parts reflex blue, 2 parts process blue, and 8 parts white. How many ounces of each of the colors of ink are needed to make 1/2 pound of blue ink?   _____

Unit 19   SCALING WITH THE PROPORTION WHEEL

BASIC PRINCIPLES

- Apply the principles of scaling with the proportion wheel to the printing and graphic communications industry by solving the practical problems in this unit.

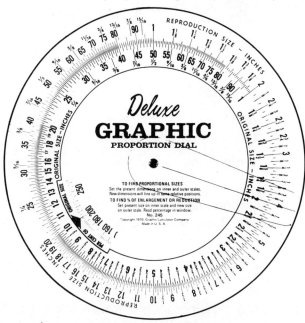

The figures on the outer circle of the wheel represent the reproduction size in inches. The figures just below these represent the original size in inches. The innermost figures represent the percent of the original. These figures may be stated in inches or picas, among other units of measure. Your answers must be stated in like manner and given to the nearest sixteenth.

The following examples show that by aligning the indicator with the original size on the inner scale with the reproduction screen on the outer scale, one can easily find the percent that is dialed into the camera when shooting the copy.

<u>Examples</u>

1.   On the proportion wheel that follows, the indicator reveals that the original size is 2″, the reproduction size if 4″, and the reproduction is 200% of the original size.

2. On the proportion wheel that follows, the indicator reveals that the original size is 5 1/4″, the reproduction size is 3 5/8″, and the reproduction is 69% of the original size.

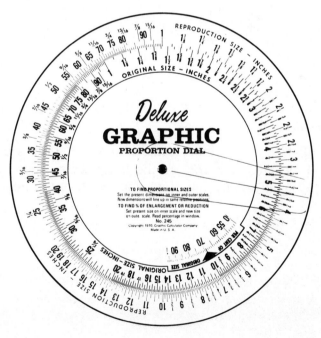

Determining Proportional Sizes

1. Set the known original dimension on the inner scale with the known reproduction dimension on the outer scale.

2. Set the indicator on the other known dimension on the appropriate scale and the unknown dimension will appear under the indicator.

Examples

1. A photo that measures 8″ × 4″ is made into a halftone 6″ wide. What is the depth of the halftone?

   (a) Line up 8″ on the inner scale with 6″ on the outer scale.
   (b) Turn the indicator to 4″ on the inner scale. The 3″ dimension lines up on the outer scale. Therefore, the depth of the halftone is 3″.

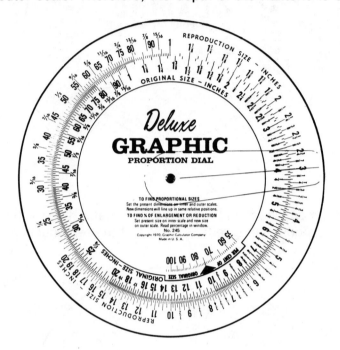

2. A snapshot that measures 2 1/8″ × 3 1/2″ is made into a halftone 1 1/4″ wide. What is the depth of the negative?

   (a) Line up 2 1/8″ on the inner scale with 1 1/4″ on the outer scale.
   (b) Turn the indicator to 3 1/2″ on the inner scale. Approximately 2 1/16″ lines up on the outer scale. Therefore, the depth of the negative is 2 1/16″.

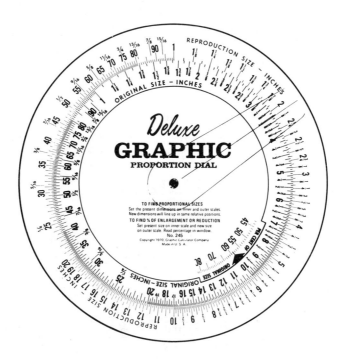

PRACTICAL PROBLEMS

A. In each of the following problems, given the original size, find the reproduction size, and the percent the reproduction is of the original size.

    1. 1″ × 3 1/4″ enlarged to 1 1/2″ × _____″, _____% of original size

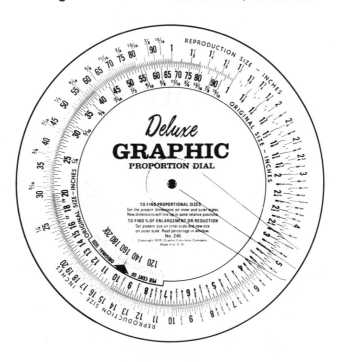

2. 2 1/2″ × 5 1/4″ reduced to 1 7/8″ × _____″, _____% of original size

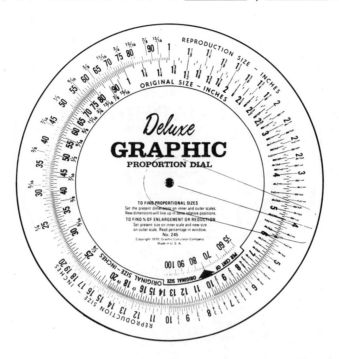

3. 1″ × 3″ reduced to _____″ × 1 7/8″, _____% of original size

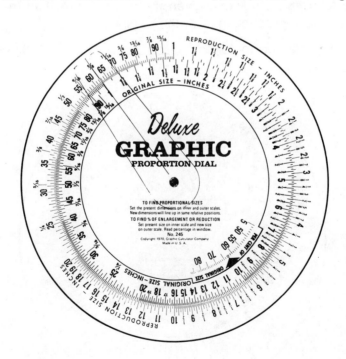

4. 5/8″ × 3″ reduced to _____″ × 1 13/16″, _____% of original size

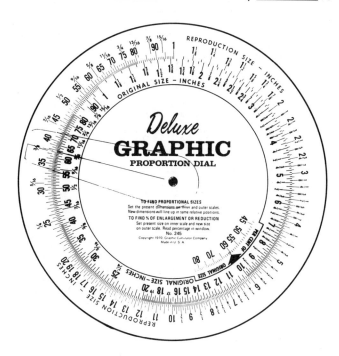

5. 2 1/2″ × 10″ enlarged to 3″ × _____″, _____% of original size

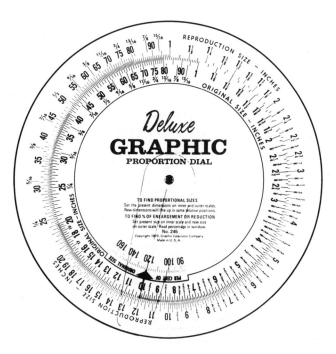

6. 3 1/8″ × 6 1/4″ enlarged to _____″ × 8″, _____% of original size

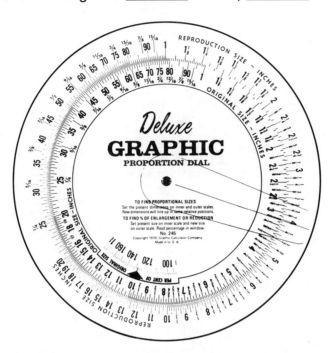

7. 4″ × 7″ enlarged to 7 5/16″ × _____″, _____% of original size

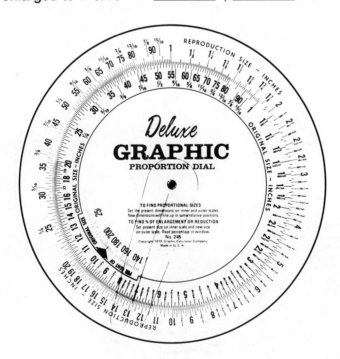

8. 3″ × 6″ enlarged to _____″ × 6 1/4″, _____% of original size

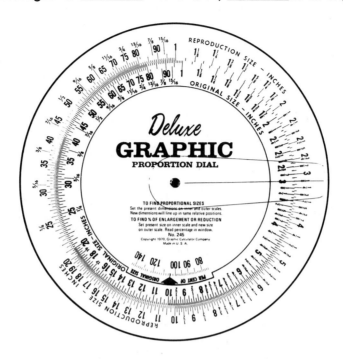

9. 1/2″ × 1 1/2″ reduced to _____″ × 15/16″, _____% of original size

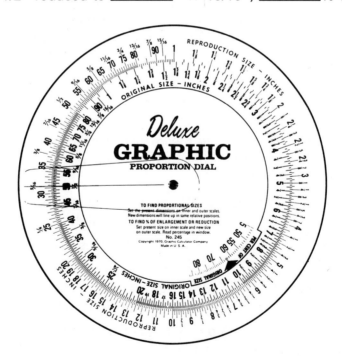

10. 3 7/8" × 4 7/8" enlarged to 7 11/16" × _____", _____% of original size

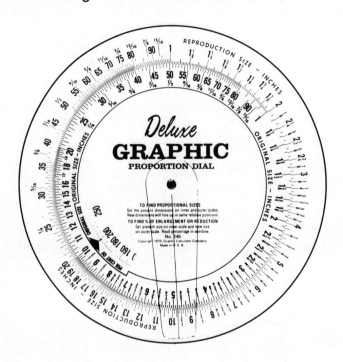

B. Use a proportion wheel to solve each of the following problems.

1. A certain photo measures 6" × 8". What size halftone should be ordered to fit a space 2 inches deep in a newspaper column?
    _____

2. A drawing is 12" × 18". A camera operator is asked to make a line negative that will fit a space 11 inches deep. How wide is the line negative?
    _____

3. A photo 5" × 6" is made into a screened print for the editorial page of a newspaper. The editorial column is 3 inches wide. How deep is the print?
    _____

4. A snapshot that measures 2 1/4" × 4 3/4" is made into a halftone 1 1/2 inches wide. What is the depth of the negative?
    _____

5. A photograph that measures 8 1/8" × 12 1/2" is made into a print 9 3/4 inches deep. What is the width?
    _____

6. If a photo measures 5" × 10", what size print should be ordered to fit a space in a newspaper column 6 inches deep?
    _____

7. How wide should a camera operator make a line negative if it is to fit a space 15 inches deep? The drawing is 10" × 16".
    _____

8. A photo 8" × 10" is made into a screened print for the editorial page of a newspaper. The editorial column is 7 inches wide. How deep is the print?
    _____

9. A snapshot that measures 4 1/2″ × 6 3/4″ is made into a halftone 2 1/2 inches wide. What is the depth of the negative?   _____

10. A photograph that measures 7 3/4″ × 15 1/8″ is made into a halftone negative measuring 9 1/8 inches deep. What is the width?   _____

Unit 20 CUSTOMARY MEASUREMENT SYSTEM

BASIC PRINCIPLES

- Apply the principles of the customary measurement system to the printing and graphic communications industry by solving the practical problems in this unit.

Linear Measurement

12 inches (in) = 1 foot (ft)	inches ÷ 12 = feet feet × 12 = inches
3 feet (ft) = 1 yard (yd)	feet ÷ 3 = yards yards × 3 = feet
36 inches (in) = 1 yard (yd)	inches ÷ 36 = yards yards × 36 = inches

Liquid Measurement

2 cups = 1 pint (pt)	cups ÷ 2 = pints pints × 2 = cups
2 pints (pt) = 1 quart (qt)	pints ÷ 2 = quarts quarts × 2 = pints
4 quarts (qt) = 1 gallon (gal)	quarts ÷ 4 = gallons gallons × 4 = quarts
8 fluidounces (fl oz) = 1 cup	ounces ÷ 8 = cups cups × 8 = ounces

Weight

16 ounces (oz) = 1 pound	ounces ÷ 16 = pounds pounds × 16 = ounces

Area

The *area* of a surface is measured in square units. The square units commonly used are the square inch or the square foot.

The *square inch* is a square that measures 1 inch on each side.

The *square foot* is a square that measures 1 foot on each side.

Since there are 12 inches in 1 foot, each side of a square foot is 12 inches long. Therefore, there are 144 square inches in a square foot.

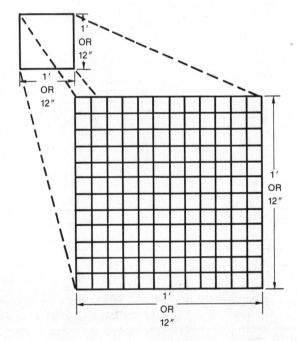

A printer usually deals with shapes that are rectangular or shapes that can be broken up into rectangular portions. To find the area of a rectangle, multiply width times length.

<u>Examples</u>

1. Find the area of a rectangle 3 1/2″ wide and 5 1/2″ long.

   Area = width × length
   = 3 1/2 × 5 1/2
   = 3.5 × 5.5
   = 19.25 sq in

2. Find the area of the figure shown.

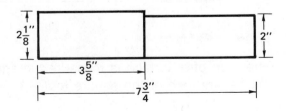

First, divide the figure into rectangles.

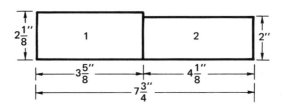

Area of rectangle [1] = 2 1/8 × 3 5/8
= 2.125 × 3.625
= 7.703125 sq in

Area of rectangle [2] = 2 × 4 1/8
= 2 × 4.125
= 8.25 sq in

Area of figure = area of rectangle [1]   7.703125 sq in
+ area of rectangle [2]   <u>+ 8.25   sq in</u>
15.953125 sq in

Practical Problems

A.   Determine the indicated measurements on the rule that follows.

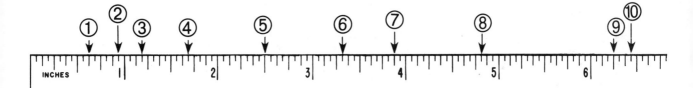

1. _____   6. _____

2. _____   7. _____

3. _____   8. _____

4. _____   9. _____

5. _____   10. _____

B. Measure the lengths indicated to the nearest eighth of an inch. Express all fractions in lowest terms.

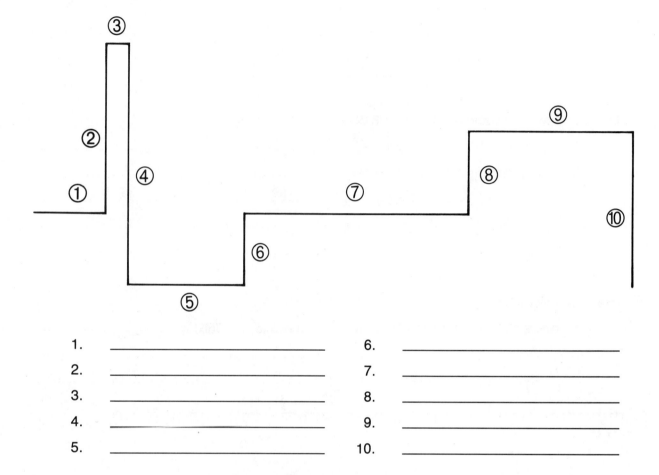

1. _____   6. _____

2. _____   7. _____

3. _____   8. _____

4. _____   9. _____

5. _____   10. _____

C. Measure the lengths indicated to the nearest sixteenth of an inch. Express all fractions in lowest terms.

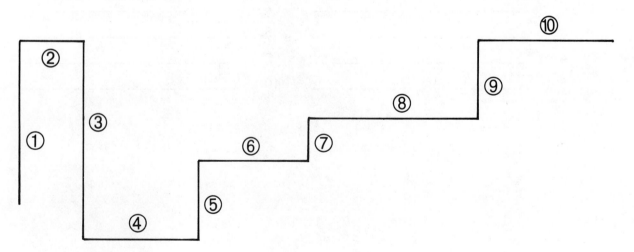

1. _____   6. _____

2. _____   7. _____

3. _____   8. _____

4. _____   9. _____

5. _____   10. _____

D. Express the following in the indicated equivalent measurement.

1.   Express 3'7" as inches.   _____

2.   Express 7" as feet.   _____

3.   Express 6'8" as inches.   _____

4.   Express 42" as yards.   _____

5.   Express 2.34 yd as feet.   _____

6.   Express 6.45' as inches.   _____

7.   Express 9 3/4" as feet.   _____

8.   Express 3.45' as inches.   _____

9.   Express 4'8" as yards.   _____

10. Express 17 1/8" as feet.   _____

E. Express the following in the indicated equivalent measurement.

1. _____ pt = 1 gal   11. _____ oz = 7.83 gal

2. _____ cups = 1 gal   12. _____ qt = 47 cups

3. _____ oz = 1 gal   13. _____ cups = 6 2/3 qt

4. _____ gal = 8 pt   14. _____ gal = 7.625 pt

5. _____ cups = 9 qt   15. _____ cups = 4.63 qt

6. _____ oz = 4 gal   16. _____ pt = 47.63 oz

7. _____ cups = 3 3/4 gal   17. _____ cups = .34 gal

8. _____ oz = 7 1/2 qt   18. _____ oz = 8 1/2 qt

9. _____ qt = 6 3/4 cups   19. _____ qt = 7.63 gal

10. _____ gal = 2.63 cups   20. _____ gal = 47.8 pt

F. Express the following in the indicated equivalent measurement.

1. 2 3/4 oz = _____ lb

2. _____ oz = 17 3/4 lb

3. 17.78 lb = _____ oz

4. _____ lb = 18 2/3 oz

5. _____ oz = 25 3/4 lb

G. Find the area of each of the following rectangles.

1. A rectangle 2 1/2″ × 3 1/2″   _____

2. A rectangle 6 1/4″ × 8 3/4″   _____

3. A rectangle 20 1/2″ × 24 3/4″   _____

4. A rectangle 3′4″ × 7′8″ (gives answer in sq ft)   _____

5. A rectangle 4′8 3/4″ × 5′7 1/2″ (give answer in sq ft) _____

6.   _____

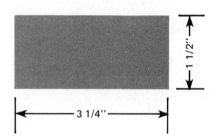

7.   _____

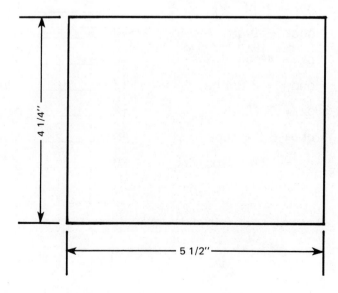

8.

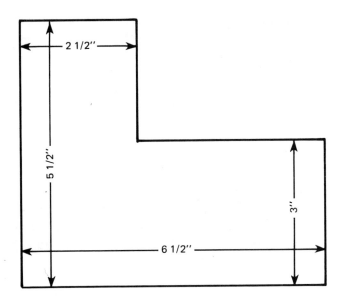

9.

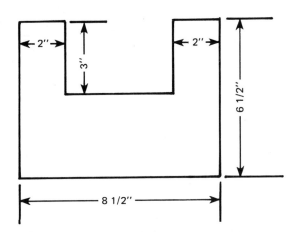

10.

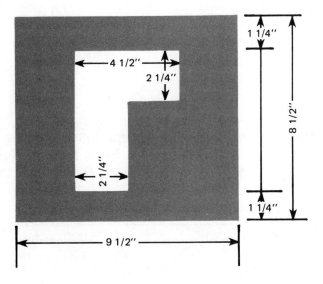

Unit 21 METRIC MEASUREMENT SYSTEM

BASIC PRINCIPLES

- Apply the principles of the metric measurement system to the printing and graphic communications industry by solving the practical problems in this unit.

Linear Measurement

The *metre* is the standard unit of linear measurement in the metric system. A metre is slightly longer than a yard. The metre (m) is subdivided into 10 equal parts called *decimetres* (dm), 100 equal parts called *centimetres* (cm), and 1000 equal parts called *millimetres* (mm).

10 millimetres (mm) = 1 centimetre (cm)	mm ÷ 10 = cm cm × 10 = mm
10 centimetres (cm) = 1 decimetre (dm)	cm ÷ 10 = dm dm × 10 = cm
10 decimetres (dm) = 1 metre (m)	dm ÷ 10 = m m × 10 = dm

Liquid Measurement

The *litre* is the standard unit of liquid measurement in the metric system. A litre is slightly larger than a quart. The litre (L) is subdivided into 1000 equal parts called *millilitres* (mL).

1 litre (L) = 1000 millilitres (mL)	mL ÷ 1000 = L L × 1000 = m

Weight

The *gram* (g) is the standard unit of weight measurement in the metric system. A gram is approximately the weight of a medium-sized paper clip. Since the gram (g) is such a small unit of weight, the kilogram (kg) is used for larger objects. There are 1000 grams (g) in 1 kilogram (kg).

1 kilogram (kg) = 1000 grams (g)	g ÷ 1000 = kg kg × 1000 = g

Area

The *area* of a surface is measured in square units. The commonly used unit is the square centimetre (cm2). The *square centimetre* (cm2) is a square that measures 1 centimetre on each side.

Since there are 10 millimetres in each centimetre, there are 100 square millimetres (mm2) in each square centimetre (cm2).

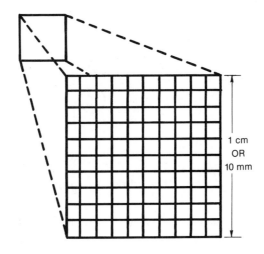

Conversion

Most of the time the printer is working in either the metric system or the customary system. When it is necessary to change from one system to the other, the appropriate formula from the following table can be used.

1 in = 2.54 cm or 25.4 mm	mm = 25.4 × in
1 cm = .3937 in	cm = 25.4 × in
1 qt = .946 L or 946 mL	in = .3937 × cm
1 L = 1.057 qt	L = qt × .946
1 lb = .454 kg or 454 g	qt = L × 1.057
1 kg = 2.204 lb	kg = .454 × lb
	lb = kg × 2.204

PRACTICAL PROBLEMS

A. **Problems 1-10.** Give the reading in centimetres and millimetres of each circled number on the rule.

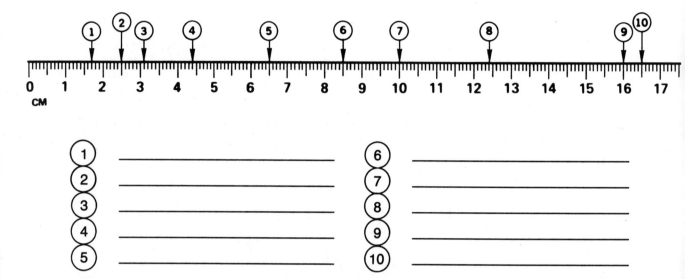

① _____		⑥ _____	
② _____		⑦ _____	
③ _____		⑧ _____	
④ _____		⑨ _____	
⑤ _____		⑩ _____	

Problems 11-20. Correctly place the following measurements on the rule.

⑪	13 cm	⑯	0.9 cm
⑫	16.5 cm	⑰	17 mm
⑬	13 mm	⑱	19.3 cm
⑭	165 mm	⑲	147 mm
⑮	9.6 cm	⑳	108 mm

B. Measure in centimetres the lengths indicated.

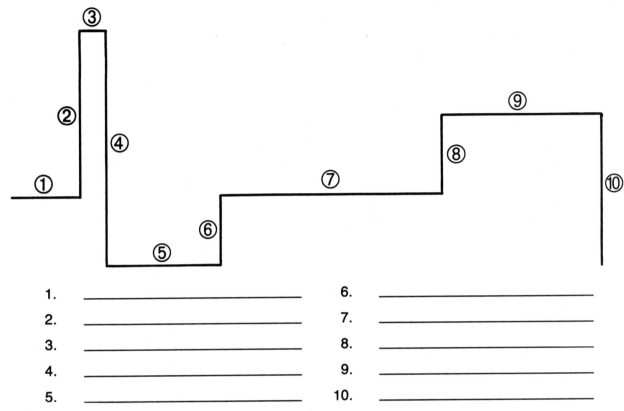

1. _____   6. _____

2. _____   7. _____

3. _____   8. _____

4. _____   9. _____

5. _____   10. _____

C. Measure in millimetres the lengths indicated.

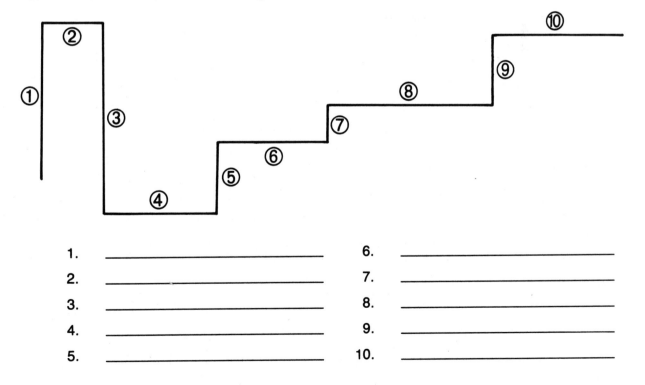

1. _____   6. _____

2. _____   7. _____

3. _____   8. _____

4. _____   9. _____

5. _____   10. _____

D. Express the following in the indicated equivalent measurement.

1. 6.3 cm = _____ mm   6. 47 mm = _____ cm

2. 75 mm = _____ cm   7. _____ mm = 57.3 cm

3. 17.8 cm = _____ mm   8. 3.2 cm = _____ mm

4. _____ mm = 19.3 cm   9. 98.5 cm = _____ mm

5. _____ cm = 153 mm   10. _____ mm = 153 cm

E. Express the following in the indicated equivalent measurement.

1. 65 mL = _____ L   6. 457 mL = _____ L

2. 0.065 L = _____ mL   7. 3.5 L = _____ mL

3. 2 L = _____ mL   8. _____ L = 485 mL

4. _____ L = 465 mL   9. _____ mL = 1.8 L

5. _____ mL = 2345 L   10. 0.2 L = _____ mL

F. Express the following in the indicated equivalent measurement.

1. 3 kg = _____ g   6. 458 g = _____ kg

2. 3.7 kg = _____ g   7. _____ g = 9.3 kg

3. _____ kg = 4300 g   8. _____ kg = 750 g

4. _____ g = 0.83 kg   9. _____ g = 0.085 kg

5. 96 g = _____ kg   10. 0.375 kg = _____ g

G. Find the area of each of the following rectangles.

1. A rectangle 18 cm × 15 cm   _____

2. A rectangle 19.3 cm × 18.6 cm   _____

3. A rectangle 23.7 cm × 35.8 cm   _____

4. A rectangle 238 mm × 465 mm (give answer in cm2)   _____

5. A rectangle 455 mm × 685 mm (give answer in cm2)   _____

6.   _____

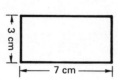

7.

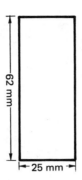

8.

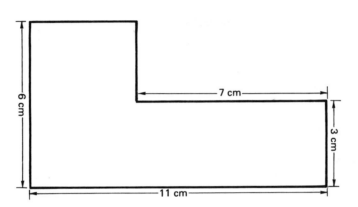

9.

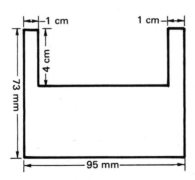

10.

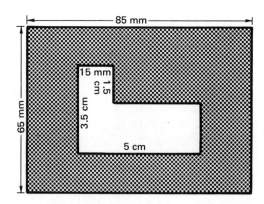

H. Express the following in the indicated equivalent measurement.

1. 14 1/2 in = _____ cm

2. 6.5 cm = _____ in

3. _____ cm = 2′ 9″

4. 4′ 7″ = _____ m

5. _____ qt = 453 mL

6. 4.5 L = _____ qt

7. _____ cups = 1.5 L

8. 4 fl oz = _____ mL

9. 5 1/2 lb = _____ kg

10. _____ lb = 475 g

Unit 22 THE MICROMETER

BASIC PRINCIPLES

- Apply the principles of the micrometer to the printing and graphic communications industry by solving the practical problems in this unit.

The *micrometer* (mike) is an instrument used to accurately measure objects to a thousandth of an inch. Micrometers that measure objects larger than an inch are available. However, the printer usually deals with the 1-inch micrometer. The 1-inch micrometer is to measure the thickness of stock.

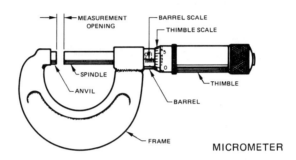

MICROMETER

The digits on the barrel of the micrometer represent .100 inch, .200 inch, .300 inch, and so on. The 4 subdivisions between the digits each represent .025 inch. Each turn of the thimble moves it from one division line to the next, or .025 inch. The numbers along the thimble indicate thousandths of an inch.

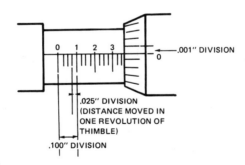

To read a mike, first determine the number of hundreds of thousandths, then add the number of .025-inch, and divisions and finally, add the thousandths of inches on the thimble.

<u>Examples</u>

1.

.200
.050
.250″

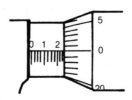

2.

.500
.050
.012

.562"

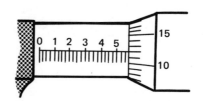

PRACTICAL PROBLEMS

Give the indicated reading for each of the following micrometers.

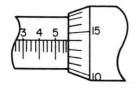

1. _____

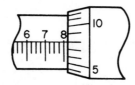

5. _____

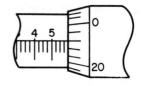

8. _____

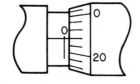

2. _____

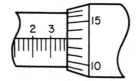

6. _____

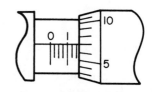

9. _____

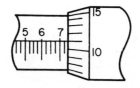

3. _____

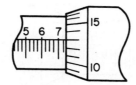

7. _____

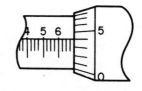

10. _____

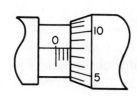

4. _____

GRAPHS AND CHARTS

Unit 23 APPLICATION OF GRAPHS AND CHARTS

BASIC PRINCIPLES

- Apply the principles of graphs and charts to the printing and graphic communications industry by solving the practical problems in this unit.

PRACTICAL PROBLEMS

1. The income of the ABC Company for a year is shown in the following graph.

    (a) What is the income for July?

    (b) What is the income for February?

    (c) What is the income for October?

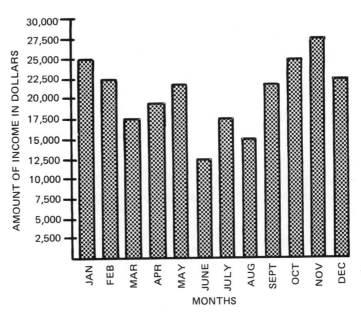

2. Draw a bar graph showing the income for a year for the XYZ Company.

January	$18,000	July	$20,000
February	$19,500	August	$18,000
March	$17,500	September	$17,500
April	$15,000	October	$19,000
May	$17,000	November	$22,000
June	$18,000	December	$21,000

3. The time required to print letterheads, catalogs, and brochures is shown in the following graph.

   (a) What is the time required for stripping an order for 10,000 catalogs?

   (b) What is the time required for binding for 10,000, 32-page catalogs?

   (c) What is the time required for typesetting 10,000, 2-color letterheads?

   (d) What is the total time required for an order of 10,000, 2-color letterheads?

   (e) What is the press time required for an order of 10,000, 2-color brochures?

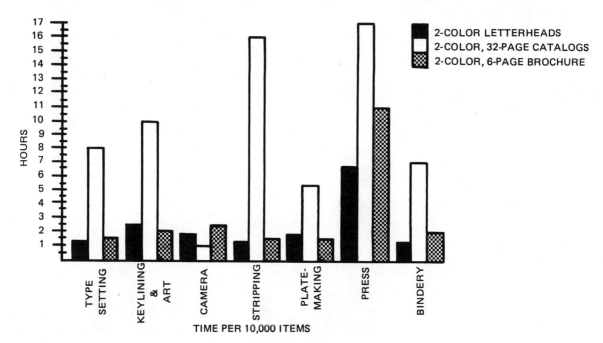

4. The following circle graph shows the distribution of income for the ABC Company. If the company has an income of $25,000 for October, give the amounts charged to labor, materials, overhead, management, and profit.

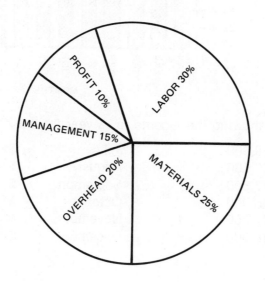

5. The XYZ Company has an income of $10,000 for a year. The costs for running the company include labor, $4000; materials, $3000; overhead $1200; management, $950; and profit the remainder. Draw a circle graph to show the percentage of each cost.

6. The following graph shows the time required for deep-etch coatings on plates to reach the same degree of hardness due to dark reaction at different relative humidities at 78°F.

    (a) How many hours does it take to reach the same degree of hardness at 60% relative humidity?

    (b) How many hours does it take to reach the same degree of hardness at 75% relative humidity?

    (c) How many hours does it take to reach the same degree of hardness at 70% relative humidity?

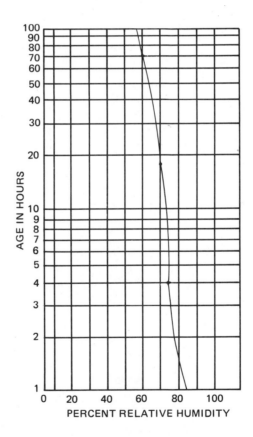

Unit 24 THE POINT SYSTEM

BASIC PRINCIPLES

- Apply the principles of the point system to the printing and graphic communications industry by solving the practical problems in this unit.

The point system was adapted in the United States in 1886. The *point,* which measures 0.01384 inch or approximately 1/72 of an inch, is used to measure thickness (height of type and vertical line spacing). The *pica* is used to measure lengths of lines or depths of area of type.

The following drawing shows an inch that is divided into seventy-two equal parts. Each division is 1/72 of an inch or one point. Twelve of these points equal one pica. Six picas equal one inch. One-half of a pica equals six points and is called a *nonpareil.*

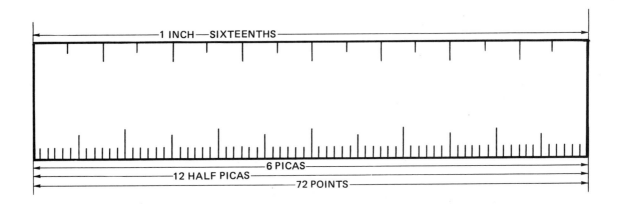

Standard Printers' Measures
72 points = 1 inch (approximately)
12 points = 1 pica (exactly)
6 picas = 1 inch (approximately)
6 points = one-half (1/2) pica (exactly)
1 point = 1/72 inch (approximately)

A line gauge that the printer uses to measure points, picas, and inches is shown in the following drawing.

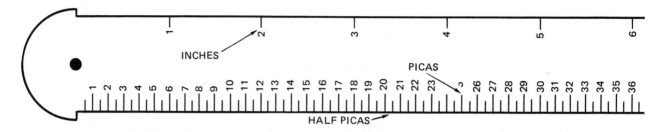

Expressing Inches as Picas and Points

To express inches as points and points as inches, inches as picas and picas as inches, and picas as points, use the following formulas:

$$
\begin{aligned}
\text{inches} \times 72 &= \text{points} \\
\text{picas} \times 12 &= \text{points} \\
\text{points} \div 12 &= \text{picas} \\
\text{inches} \times 6 &= \text{picas} \\
\text{points} \div 72 &= \text{inches} \\
\text{picas} \div 6 &= \text{inches}
\end{aligned}
$$

Note: When expressing inches as picas, use 6 picas to the inch as an exact measurement to simplify your computations. For example, a 10-inch measurement equals 60 picas.

Examples

1. The depth of the copy is 2 3/4 inches. Give the depth of the copy in points.

   2 3/4 inches × 72 points per inch = 198 points

2. A form measures 39 picas wide. Give the width of the form in inches and also in points.

   39 picas ÷ 6 picas per inch = 6 1/2 inches
   39 picas × 12 points per pica = 468 points

Adding Picas and Points

Addition of picas and points can be used when figuring tab parameters for columnar forms. Accuracy is vital to the speedy setting of this type. Another application of addition of picas and points is the proper spacing of lines of type.

When adding picas and points, express the picas and points as points, add the points together, and then express this total as picas and points.

Examples

1. Add 12 picas and 5 points, 7 picas and 9 points, and 19 picas and 8 points.

12 picas and 5 points	=	149 points
7 picas and 9 points	=	93 points
19 picas and 8 points	=	+ 236 points
		478 points

   Express 478 points as picas and points.

   478 ÷ 12 = 39 picas and 10 points

You may wish to add the picas and points separately and then express the points as picas and points.

2.
12 picas	5 points
7 picas	9 points
+ 19 picas	8 points
38 picas	22 points

   22 points = 1 pica and 10 points

38 picas	
+ 1 pica	10 points
39 picas and 10 points	

Subtracting Picas and Points

Subtraction of picas and points is often used to calculate the amount of space remaining to be filled in a line of type.

When subtracting picas and points, express the picas and points as points, subtract the points, and then express this remainder as picas and points.

Examples

1. Subtract 16 picas and 8 points from 25 picas and 6 points.

25 picas and 6 points	=	306 points
16 picas and 8 points	=	− 200 points
		106 points

   Express 106 points as picas and points.

   106 ÷ 12 = 8 picas and 10 points

You may wish to subtract the picas and points separately. If necessary, borrow 12 points (1 pica) from the picas column.

2. 25 picas and 6 points =
24 picas and 18 points	
− 16 picas and 8 points	
8 picas and 10 points	

Multiplying Picas and Points

To find the total width of columnar copy, it is necessary to multiply equal column widths by the number of columns needed. To find the depth of a page, it is necessary to multiply the number of lines by the point size plus the leading (space between the lines).

To multiply picas and points, express the picas as points and multiply. Divide by 12 to express the answer as picas and points.

Examples

    1. Multiply 9 picas and 4 points by 4.

        9 picas and 4 points =   112 points

                                ×   4

                               448 points

      448 ÷ 12 = 37 picas and 4 points

You may wish to multiply the picas and points by a whole number. This is done by multiplying the picas by the whole number and the points by the whole number, expressing the points as picas and points, and then adding to obtain the answer.

    2. Multiply 6 picas and 4 points by 7.

        6 picas × 7 = 42 picas; 4 points × 7 = 28 points

        28 points = 2 picas and 4 points

          42 picas

      + 2 picas and 4 points

          44 picas and 4 points

Dividing Picas and Points

Division of picas and points is one of the necessary operations in the many problems arising in copyfitting.

Dividing a line length given in picas and points by a whole number (number of columns) gives the width of each column in picas and points.

To divide picas and points by a whole number, express the picas as points, divide by the number of columns, and express the answer as picas and points.

Examples

    1. Divide 76 picas and 6 points by 6 columns.

        76 picas and 6 points = 918 points

        918 ÷ 6 columns = 153 points

        153 points ÷ 12 points per pica = 12 picas and 9 points

To find the number of columns that are available in any given width, it is necessary to divide picas and points by picas and points. To find the number of lines on a given page, use the same method.

2. How many columns of figures 3 1/2 picas wide can be fit into 35 picas?

   35 × 12 = 420 points, 3 1/2 × 12 = 42 points
   420 ÷ 42 = 10 columns

3. There are 14 galleys of type measuring 108 picas each. If this type is divided into 28 pages, how many picas of type are on each page? Have an equal number of picas on each page.

   108 × 14 = 1512 picas
   1512 ÷ 28 = 54 picas on each page

PRACTICAL PROBLEMS

A. Answer each of the following problems. Be sure to give the answer in the indicated measurement.

   1. The following ad measures 4″ × 3 3/4″. What is the size in picas of the ad? _____

   ### WEEK-END CRUISE
   Aboard the
   ### "S.S. PRINCESS"
   Every Friday — 4:30 P.M.

   ● *Refreshments*
   ● *Dancing*
   ● *Music*

   $175.00 per couple **$105.00** single
   Call 898-5433 for Reservations
   ### Sanders Wharf
   Cordova, Mass.

   2. The depth of the copy is 4 3/4 inches. Find its depth in picas and points. _____

   3. What part of an inch is 6 points? What part of a pica is 6 points? _____

   4. A form measures 288 points wide. Find its width in inches and in picas. _____

   5. What part of an inch is 54 points? _____

   6. A line of type measures 17 picas. Find its length in inches and in points. _____

   7. A line of type is 42 picas long. Find its length in inches and in points. _____

   8. A form measures 5 7/8″ wide × 5 5/8″ deep. Find its size in picas and points. _____

9. A job is printed on stock cut 8 1/2″ wide × 11″ deep. Find its size in picas. _____

10. For a certain job, 114 lines need to be ruled. If the length of each line is 216 points, how many total inches of rule are needed for this job? _____

B. In each of the following problems, use addition to find the answer.

1. Add 3 picas and 3 points; 12 picas; 12 picas and 3 points; and 12 picas and 6 points. _____

2. Add 11 picas and 4 points; 16 picas and 10 points; and 21 picas and 8 points. _____

3. Add 23 picas and 9 points; 45 picas and 3 points; and 19 picas and 7 points. _____

4. Add 15 picas and 8 points; 52 picas and 5 points; and 34 picas and 9 points. _____

5. Add 17 picas and 2 points; 68 picas and 10 points; and 33 picas and 9 points. _____

6. Add 10 picas and 6 points; 2 picas; 7 picas and 5 points; 7 picas and 9 points; 7 picas and 3 points; 7 picas and 6 points; 7 picas and 9 points; 7 picas and 3 points; and 12 picas and 6 points. _____

7. Add 10 picas and 11 points, 6 picas and 10 points, 7 picas and 3 points, and 10 picas. _____

8. Add 5 picas and 7 points; 1 pica; 5 picas and 7 points; 1 pica; 5 picas and 7 points; 1 pica; 5 picas and 7 points; 1 pica; 5 picas and 7 points; 1 pica; 5 picas and 7 points; 1 pica; and 5 picas and 6 points. _____

9. Add 4 picas and 6 points; 3 picas; 4 picas and 6 points; 3 picas; 4 picas and 6 points; 3 picas; 4 picas and 6 points; and 3 picas. _____

10. Add 12 picas and 4 points; 2 picas and 10 points; 5 points; 2 picas and 10 points; 4 points; 2 picas and 10 points; 5 points, 2 picas and 10 points; 4 points; and 2 picas and 10 points. _____

C. In each of the following problems, use subtraction to find the answer.

1. Subtract 15 picas and 9 points from 34 picas and 7 points. _____

2. Subtract 23 picas and 8 points from 63 picas and 3 points. _____

3. Subtract 32 picas and 5 points from 45 picas and 2 points. _____

4. Subtract 19 picas and 11 points from 39 picas and 5 points. _____

5. Subtract 1 pica and 11 points from 4 picas and 10 points. _____

6. Subtract 11 picas and 7 points from 36 picas. _____

7. Subtract 10 picas and 6 points from 44 picas and 3 points. _____

8. Subtract 1 pica and 9 points from 39 picas and 6 points. _____

9. Subtract 13 picas and 7 points from 25 picas and 6 points. _____

10. Subtract 21 picas and 11 points from 45 picas. _____

D. In each of the following problems, use the appropriate operations to find the answer.

1. What is the total width of copy if it has 9 columns, each 2 picas and 10 points wide? _____

2. What is the total width of copy if it has 8 columns, each 3 picas and 4 points wide? _____

ALPHABET LENGTH IN POINTS	CHAR. PER PICA	ALPHABET LENGTH IN POINTS	CHAR. PER PICA	ALPHABET LENGTH IN POINTS	CHAR. PER PICA	ALPHABET LENGTH IN POINTS	CHAR. PER PICA
60 PTS	5.70	102 PTS	3.35	144 PTS	2.38	186 PTS	1.84
61 PTS	5.61	103 PTS	3.32	145 PTS	2.36	187 PTS	1.83
62 PTS	5.52	104 PTS	3.29	146 PTS	2.34	188 PTS	
63 PTS	5.43	105					

3. What is the total width of copy if it has 5 columns, each 10 picas and 3 points wide? _____

4. What is the total depth of copy if it has 40 lines, each 11 points deep? _____

5. What is the total depth of copy if it has 36 lines of type, each 14 points deep? _____

6. What is the total width of copy if it has 12 columns, each 1 pica and 7 points wide? _____

7. What is the total depth of copy if it has 27 lines of type, each 9 points deep? _____

8. What is the total depth of copy if it has 25 lines of type, each 18 points deep? _____

9. What is the total depth of copy if it has 150 pages, each 45 picas deep? _____

10. What is the total depth of copy if it has 45 pages, each 27 picas and 10 points deep? _____

E. In each of the following problems, use the appropriate operations to find the answer.

1. How many columns 3 picas and 9 points wide can be fit into 45 picas? _____

2. How many columns 2 1/2 picas wide can be fit into 27 1/2 picas? _____

3. If 8 columns fit evenly into 45 picas, what is the width of each column? _____

4. What is the length of each page in picas if 32 pages have a total length of 1280 picas? _____

5. How many columns 4 picas and 6 points wide can be fit into 45 picas? _____

6. If 15 columns, each 2 picas and 3 points wide, are fit into 36 picas, what is the space between the columns? _____

7. How many lines of 10-point type set solid (no space between the lines) can be obtained from copy measuring 8 3/4 inches deep? _____

8. A book has pages of type 50 picas deep. How many pages are contained in the book if the total number of picas is 10,278? _____

9. How many lines of 8-point type set solid (no space between the lines) are needed to fill a book containing 64 pages if each page is 36 picas deep? _____

10. A form with 9 columns fits in a space 40 picas wide. The first column is 9 picas and 4 points wide, and the other columns are 3 picas and 6 points wide. The space between the columns is even. How wide is each space? _____

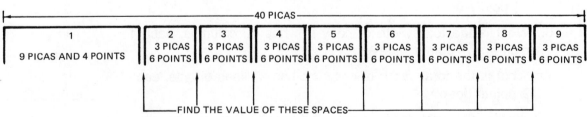

Unit 25 THE EM

BASIC PRINCIPLES

- Apply the principles of the em to the printing and graphic communications industry by solving the practical problems in this unit.

The em is an important part of the measuring system in typesetting. The *em* is a printer's unit of measure equal to the square of the type size. The width of the em does vary slightly according to the design of the various type styles. This variance is not considered in the examples in this text.

1 SQUARE EM

In printing, all paragraph indentations are made with the em. When indenting paragraphs or setting type where figures and punctuation occur, the typesetter uses the *en,* which is one-half of the em, or the *thin space,* which is one-third of the em.

EN = $\frac{1}{2}$ EM   THIN SPACE = $\frac{1}{3}$ EM

The length of an em must also be known when setting blank lines on form work. The phototypesetting equipment can only set full ems for baseline ruling.

Determining the Number of Ems of Type in a Line

1. Express the length of the line in points.

2. Divide by the size of the type used.

Examples

1. Find the number of ems in a line of 8-point type that measures 2 inches wide.

   Express the length of the line in points.
   2 × 72 = 144 points (72 points = 1 inch)
   Divide by 8 since 8-point type is used.
   144 ÷ 8 = 18 ems in the line

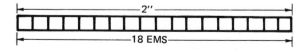

2. Find the number of ems in a line of 14-point type that is 54 picas long.

Express the length of the line in points.
54 × 12 = 648 points (12 points = 1 pica)
Divide by 14 since 14-point type is used.
648 ÷ 14 = 46.3 ems in the line

Determining the Length of the Line

1. Multiply the number of ems by the size of type to determine the number of points per line.

2. Divide by 12 to determine the number of picas or divide by 72 to determine the number of inches.

<u>Examples</u>

1. What is the length in inches of a line of 8-point type containing 45 ems?

Determine the number of points in the line.
45 × 8 = 360 points
360 ÷ 72 = 5″

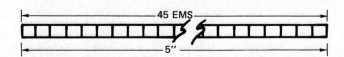

2. What is the pica length of a line of 36-point type containing 55 ems?

Determine the number of points in the line.
55 × 36 = 1980 points
1980 ÷ 12 = 165 picas

Determining the Pica Depth of a Page (Set Solid) in Picas and Points

1. Multiply the number of lines by the size of type to determine the point depth.

2. Divide by 12 (12 points = 1 pica).

<u>Examples</u>

1. Find the pica depth of a page of 8-point type that is 20 lines deep set solid.

To determine point depth:
20 × 8 = 160 points
To determine pica and point depth:
160 ÷ 12 = 13 picas 4 points

2. Find the pica depth of a page of 14-point type that is 36 lines deep set solid.

To determine point depth:
36 × 14 = 504 points
To determine pica and point depth:
504 ÷ 12 = 42 picas

Determining the Number of Lines in a Page (Set Solid)

1. Find the point depth.

2. Divide by the size of type used.

<u>Examples</u>

1. How many lines of type are contained in 4 inches of type set solid in 12-point type?

Find the point depth:
4 × 72 = 288 points
288 ÷ 12 = 24 lines on the page

2. How many lines of type are contained in a page 32 picas deep and set solid in 8-point type?

Find the point depth:
32 × 12 = 384 points
384 ÷ 8 = 48 lines on the page

Determining the Number of Ems in a Page (Set Solid)

1. Find the number of lines in the page if this information is not given.

2. Find the number of ems in 1 line.

3. Multiply the ems in 1 line by the number of lines to determine the number of ems in a page.

<u>Examples</u>

1. Find the number of ems in a page 25 lines long and 16 picas wide, set in 8-point type.

$$\frac{16 \text{ picas} \times 12 \text{ points}}{8 \text{ points}} = 24 \text{ ems in 1 line}$$

24 × 25 = 600 ems in the page

2. Find the number of ems in a page 8 inches long and 30 picas wide, set in 18-point type.

$$\frac{8 \text{ inches} \times 72 \text{ points}}{18 \text{ points}} = 32 \text{ lines on the page}$$

$$\frac{30 \text{ picas} \times 12 \text{ points}}{18 \text{ points}} = 20 \text{ ems in 1 line}$$

$20 \times 32 = 640$ ems in the page

PRACTICAL PROBLEMS

A.   In each of the following problems, find the number of ems.

1.   How many ems of 6-point type can be set in a line that measures 11 picas?   _____

2.   Find the number of ems of 14-point type contained in a line set 7 inches wide.   _____

3.   The title on a program measures 3 3/4 inches. If the title is set in 18-point type, how many ems does it contain?   _____

4.   A line of 8-point type measures 24 picas. How many ems are contained in the line?   _____

5.   If a line of 6-point type measures 24 picas, how many ems does it contain?   _____

6.   How many ems of 12-point type can be set in a line that measures 26 picas.   _____

7.   A line of 8-point type measures 4 1/2 inches. How many ems are contained in the line?   _____

8.   Find the number of ems of 6-point type contained in a line set 5 1/2 inches wide.   _____

9.   How many ems of 18-point type can be set in a line that measures 25 picas?   _____

10. Find the number of ems of 14-point type contained in a line set to a width of 7 inches.   _____

B.   In each of the following problems, find the length of the line of type.

1.   Find the length in inches of a line of 8-point type containing 54 ems.   _____

2.   Find the length in inches of a line of 12-point type containing 60 ems.   _____

3. A line of 18-point type contains 98 ems. What is the length of the line in picas? _____

4. A line of 10-point type contains 72 ems. What is the length of the line in picas? _____

5. Find the length in inches of a line of 4-point type containing 90 ems. _____

6. A line of 30-point type contains 6 ems. What is the length of the line in picas? _____

7. A line of 14-point type contains 36 ems. What is the length of the line in picas? _____

8. Find the length in inches of a line of 12-point type containing 96 ems. _____

9. Find the length in inches of a line of 8-point type containing 66 ems. _____

10. A line of 18-point type contains 54 ems. What is the length of the line in picas? _____

C. In each of the following problems, find the pica depth of the page (type is set solid).

1. What is the pica depth of a page of 6-point type that is 136 lines long? _____

2. Find the pica depth of a page of 14-point type that is 24 lines long. _____

3. Find the pica depth of a page of 12-point type that is 5 inches long. _____

4. What is the pica depth of a page of 24-point type that is 15 inches long? _____

5. Find the pica depth of a page of 18-point type that is 50 lines long. _____

6. What is the pica depth of a page of 10-point type that is 42 lines long? _____

7. What is the pica depth of a page of 8-point type that is 9 1/2 inches long? _____

8. Find the pica depth of a page of 6-point type, that is 8 inches long. _____

9. Find the pica depth of a page of 24-point type that is 19 lines long. _____

10. Find the pica depth of a page of 14-point type that is 12 1/2 inches long. _____

D. In each of the following problems, find the number of lines in the page.

    1. How many lines of 8-point type are contained in a galley of type 21 inches long? _____

    2. How many lines of 8-point type are contained in a type page 48 picas deep? _____

    3. How many lines of 8-point type are contained in a type page 36 picas deep? _____

    4. How many lines of 12-point type are contained in a type page 40 picas deep? _____

    5. How many lines of 6-point type are contained in a galley of machine-set type measuring 10 inches? _____

    6. A column of type in a newspaper measures 18 inches. How many lines of 8-point type are contained in the column? _____

    7. How many lines of 9-point type are contained in a galley of type 51 picas long? _____

    8. How many lines of 18-point type are contained in a type page 6 inches deep? _____

    9. How many lines of 10-point type are contained in a type page 75 picas deep? _____

    10. How many lines of 6-point type are contained in a galley of machine-set type measuring 12 3/4 inches? _____

E. In each of the following problems, find the number of ems on the page.

    1. Find the number of ems in a page 20 lines long and 19 picas wide, set in 8-point type. _____

    2. Find the number of ems in a page 16 lines long and 5 inches wide, set in 10-point type. _____

    3. Find the number of ems in a page 7 inches long and 28 picas wide, set in 14-point type. _____

    4. Find the number of ems in a page 64 picas long and 6 inches wide, set in 8-point type. _____

    5. Find the number of ems in a page 51 picas long and 36 picas wide, set in 18-point type. _____

    6. Find the number of ems in a page 6 inches long and 4 1/2 inches wide, set in 12-point type. _____

    7. Find the number of ems in a page 25 lines long and 11 inches wide, set in 5 1/2-point type. _____

8. Find the number of ems in a page 62 picas long and 47 picas wide, set in 6-point type.   _____

9. Find the number of ems in a page 33 picas long and 2 1/2 inches wide, set in 9-point type.   _____

10. Find the number of ems in a page 2 inches long and 9 picas wide, set in 6-point type.   _____

11. Find the number of ems in a page 29 lines long and 13 picas wide, set in 12-point type.   _____

12. Find the number of ems in a page 6 inches long and 36 picas wide, set in 12-point type.   _____

13. Find the number of ems in a page 5 inches long and 10 inches wide, set in 10-point type.   _____

14. Find the number of ems in a page 50 picas long and 42 picas wide, set in 8-point type.   _____

15. Find the number of ems in a page 40 lines long and 20 picas wide, set in 14-point type.   _____

16. Find the number of ems in a page 35 picas long and 27 picas wide, set in 12-point type.   _____

17. Find the number of ems in a page 13 lines long and 2 1/2 inches wide, set in 6-point type.   _____

18. Find the number of ems in a page 35 picas long and 2 1/2 inches wide, set in 10-point type.   _____

19. Find the number of ems in a page 18 lines long and 15 picas wide, set in 6-point type.   _____

20. Find the number of ems in a page 4 inches long and 2 2/3 inches wide, set in 8-point type.   _____

Unit 26 LEADED LINES

BASIC PRINCIPLES

- Apply the principles of leaded lines to the printing and graphic communications industry by solving the practical problems in this unit.

In order to make printed material easier to read, and to set off certain parts for emphasis, spaces are usually left between the lines of type. In the days when it was more popular and cost effective to use hand-set type or line-cast type in the printing process, lines of type were spaced by inserting material called *leads.* Today, this spacing between lines is still referred to as *leading.*

Too much leading causes the printed message to look awkward. Not enough leading causes problems with lines of type overlapping each other. As little as one-half point of leading may be used between lines of type. However, 1 or 2 points are commonly used between lines for ease of reading, as well as making the correction process easier.

Printers refer to type as set 8 on 10 (8/10) if the point size of type is 8 and 2 extra points of leading are used between the lines of type. Type that is set 10 on 11 (10/11) indicates 10-point type with 1 extra point of leading.

Note: When figuring the depth of any type area, count the number of lines and subtract 1 to find the number of spaces needed. (e.g., 12 lines of type have 11 spaces.)

Determining the Pica Depth of a Page

1. Determine the point depth of the page by multiplying the number of lines by the point size of the type, multiplying the number of spaces by the points of leading, and then adding. (Remember that there is 1 less space than the number of lines on the page.)

2. Divide by 12 to find the pica depth (12 points = 1 pica).

Examples

1. Find the pica depth of a page of 8-point type with 2 extra points of leading per line. The block of copy is 24 lines long.

   Determine the point depth.
   (24 × 8) + (23 × 2) = 238 points
   Determine the pica depth.
   238 ÷ 12 = 19 picas 10 points

2. What is the pica depth of a page of 9-point type set on 12 (3-point leading)? The page is 30 lines long.

   Determine the point depth.
   (30 × 9) + (29 × 3) = 357 points
   Determine the pica depth.
   357 ÷ 12 = 29 picas 9 points

Determining the Number of Lines in a Page

1. Determine the depth in points by multiplying the depth of the page by 12 (if depth is given in picas), or by multiplying the depth of the page by 72 (if depth is given in inches).

2. Divide by the type size plus the leading to find the lines per page.

3. Check the number of lines.

<u>Examples</u>

1. How many lines of 10-point type with 2 extra points of leading are contained in a page of type measuring 4 inches?

   Determine the point depth.
   $4 \times 72 = 288$ points
   Determine the number of lines.
   $288 \div (10 + 2) = 24$ lines per page
   Check
   24 lines $= (24 \times 10) + (23 \times 2) = 286$ points
   Since there are 288 points, there are 24 lines.

2. How many lines of type are contained in a page 54 picas and 8 points long, if the page is set in 6-point type and has 4 extra points of leading for each line?

   Determine the point depth.
   $54 \times 12 + 8 = 656$ points
   Determine the number of lines.
   $656 \div (6 + 4) = 65.6$ lines
   Check
   65 lines $= (65 \times 6) + (64 \times 4) = 646$ points
   66 lines $= (66 \times 6) + (65 \times 4) = 656$ points

   Since there are 656 points, there are 66 lines.

Determining the Number of Ems in a Page

1. Find the number of lines on the page.

2. Find the number of ems in 1 line (use only full ems).

3. Multiply the number of ems in 1 line by the number of lines to obtain the number of ems in the page.

<u>Examples</u>

1. Find the number of ems in a page 20 picas wide and 31 picas and 10 points deep set in 6-point type using 2 extra points of leading for each line.

   Find the depth in points.
   $(31 \times 12 + 10) = 382$ points

Find the number of lines.

(382) ÷ (6 + 2) = 47.75 lines per page

Round to 48 lines.

48 lines = (48 × 6) + (47 × 2) = 382 points

Since the depth is 382 points, we have proved 48 lines.

Find the ems per line.

(20 × 12) ÷ 6 = 40 ems per line

Find the ems per page.

40 × 48 = 1920 ems per page

2. Find the number of ems in a page 10 inches wide and 10 1/2 inches deep set 12 on 14.

Find the depth in points.

(10 1/2 × 72) = 756 points

Find the number of lines.

(756) ÷ (12 + 2) = 54 lines per page

54 lines = (54 × 12) + (53 × 2) = 754 points

Since the depth is 756 points, we have proved 54 lines.

Find the ems per line.

(10 × 72) ÷ 12 = 60 ems per line

Find the ems per page.

54 × 60 = 3240 ems per page

PRACTICAL PROBLEMS

A. In the following problems, find the pica depth of each page.

1. Find the pica depth of a page of 6-point type with 2 extra points of leading, 20 lines long. _____

2. Find the pica depth of a page of 8-point type with 2 extra points of leading, 15 lines long. _____

3. Find the pica depth of a page of 10-point type with 2 extra points of leading, 30 lines long. _____

4. Find the pica depth of a page of 12-point type with 2 extra points of leading, 40 lines long. _____

5. Find the pica depth of a page of 5 1/2-point type with 2 extra points of leading, 15 lines long. _____

6. Find the pica depth of a page of 14-point type set on 16 points, 25 lines long. _____

7. What is the pica depth of a page of 18-point type set on 24 points, 16 lines long? _____

8. What is the pica depth of a page of 24-point type with 6 extra points of leading, 22 lines long? _____

9. What is the pica depth of a page of 12-point type with 4 extra points of leading, 30 lines long? _____

10. What is the pica depth of a page of 9-point type with 3 extra points of leading, 29 lines long? _____

B. In the following problems, find the number of lines of type.

1. How many lines of 8-point type with 2 extra points of leading are contained in a galley of type 6 1/4 inches long? _____

2. How many lines of 8-point type with 2 extra points of leading are contained in a typed page 48 picas deep? _____

3. A column of type in a newspaper measures 10 1/2 inches. How many lines of 10-point type with 2 extra points of leading are contained in the column? _____

4. How many lines of type are contained in a page 24 picas long and set in 6-point type with 2 extra points of leading? _____

5. How many lines of type are contained in 3 1/2 inches of type set in 12-point type with 4 extra points of leading? _____

6. How many lines of type are contained in a page 33 picas long and set in 9-point type with 2 extra points of leading? _____

7. How many lines of type are contained in a page 5 1/2 inches long set in 6-point type with 6 extra points of leading? _____

8. How many lines of type are contained in a page 44 picas long and set in 14-point type with 2 extra points of leading? _____

9. How many lines of type are contained in a page 49 picas long and set in 8-point type with 6 extra points of leading? _____

10. How many lines of type are contained in a page 7 1/2 inches long set in 18-point type with 2 extra points of leading? _____

C. In the following problems, find the number of ems of type.

1. A form measures 21 picas wide and 33 picas deep. How many ems of 10 on 12 types does the form contain? _____

2. Find the number of ems contained in a form 4 1/2 inches wide and 2 1/3 inches deep set in 4-point type with 2 extra points of leading. _____

3. How many ems are contained in a form 24 picas wide and 56 picas deep set in 6-point type with 2 extra points of leading? _____

4. How many ems of 8-point type with 2 extra points of leading are set in a leaflet having 4 pages, if each page is printed with forms 5 inches wide and 7 1/2 inches deep? _____

5. A 4-page folder is set in 6 on 8. The type area of each page measures 4" × 6". How many ems of type does the job contain? _____

6. A short story in a magazine takes up 16 pages. Each page is printed in 2 columns, each 19 picas wide and 9 inches deep. How many ems are contained in the story if it is set 10 on 12?

        _____

7. How many ems are set in a form 4 1/4″ × 7 1/4″ if 8-point type with 2 extra points of leading is used?

        _____

8. A 4-page form, each page measuring 21 × 30 picas, is set in 8-point type with 2 extra points of leading between the lines. How many ems are contained in the 4-page form?

        _____

9. Find the number of ems contained in a form 27 picas wide by 319 picas deep, set 8 on 12.

        _____

10. A booklet is printed in 6-point type with 2 extra points of leading. The pages of the booklet measure 26 × 34 picas. How many ems are contained in the booklet if it contains 26 pages?

        _____

Unit 27 FITTING COPY TO SPACE AND SPACE TO COPY

BASIC PRINCIPLES

- Apply the principles of copyfitting to the printing and graphic communications industry by solving the practical problems in this unit.

Copyfitting is a procedure for determining how much area on a page(s) a certain manuscript will occupy when set in type.

Initially, manuscripts are often handwritten, but are ultimately typeset (printer's type). Determining the number of handwritten characters in a manuscript is difficult and time consuming. Because the characters in typewritten copy are evenly spaced, they are more easily counted.

Correct copyfitting enables the typographer to transfer typed copy into appropriate text material that is easily read and that also fits a specific area of the printed piece.

Determining the Space Needed for Copy

Use the following procedure to determine the space needed for copy.

1. Calculate the number of characters in the manuscript.
2. Select a style and size of type and determine the number of characters per pica. This text uses the chart method.
3. Select a copy width.
4. Calculate the number of lines that can fit on 1 page.
5. Calculate the number of pages needed, if more than 1 page.

Determining the Number of Characters in a Manuscript

The difference between an elite line of type and a pica line of type is shown below.

```
This is an example of Pica size type.

This is an example of Elite size type.
```

Notice the difference in the number of characters per inch. The elite type has 12 characters per inch, and the pica type has 10 characters per inch.

To determine the total number of characters in a typewritten manuscript, use the following procedure.

1. Draw a vertical line through one of the shorter lines on the typewritten page (not one of the shorter lines at the very end of each paragraph).

2. Determine the number of characters to the left of the line. Measure or actually count each character, space, and punctuation mark. Remember the elite type has 12 characters per inch, and pica type has 10 characters per inch.

3. Multiply the characters in 1 line times the total number of lines to obtain the total number of characters to the left of the line. Count all short lines as full lines so there is adequate space for the finished type.

4. Count all the characters to the right of the line.

5. Add the total number of characters to the left of the line and the total number of characters to the right of the line to determine the total number of characters in the manuscript.

For more accurate copyfitting, follow this procedure paragraph by paragraph.

Examples

1. Find the total number of characters in the following manuscript.

←——————————— 55 CHARACTERS ———————————→|	
Eric Hoffer says, "It is evident, therefore, that |if we	5
are to awaken and cultivate the talents dormant in a wh|ole	3
population we must change our concepts of what is effic|ient,	5
useful, practical, wasteful, and so on," and he goes on| to	3
say, "Up to now in this country we are warned not to wa|ste	3
our time but we are brought up to waste our lives."	0
What should be done? What can we do?	0
Vocational education has a unique opportunity to s|tep	3
in and guide the student into an area that will make hi|s	1
life more meaningful, productive and useful not only to|	0
himself but to all who come in contact with him. It can |help	4
to shape the student into a creative individual that is|	0
capable of coping with the ever-increasing challenge of| the	4
changing technology.	0
total	31

55 characters x 14 lines = 770 characters (to the
left of the line)

Add 770 characters
     31 characters (to the right of the line)
    801 characters total

2. Find the total number of characters in the following manuscript.

← ——————— 69 CHARACTERS ——————— →	
The Printers' Paper Catalog and Price List plays a vital role in the printing estimator's workaday life. Because of this, the student must know more about the information contained in it.	_1_ _0_ _0_
One of the more difficult tasks is helping the printing buyer judge the quality of a given paper. But once a particular type and weight of sheet has been selected, you will find there are a number of alternatives available. With the help of the paper catalog and paper sample books, the selection of the right stock will become easier.	_4_ _2_ _4_ _1_ _0_
Paper, which constitutes a major expenditure in any job, has to be figured very carefully. To help you understand this fact and enable you to pick the appropriate paper stock, this book is being written.	_3_ _3_ _0_
	total _18_

69 characters X 11 lines = 759 characters (to the left of the line)

Add 759 characters
+ _18_ characters (to the right of the line)
777 characters total

Determining the Number of Characters Per Pica

Type varies in style and size, as shown below. For this reason, it is necessary to determine the number of characters per pica. The following are the three methods of determining the number of characters per pica.

Palatino
12 POINT

Helvetica Bold
18 POINT

Lisbon Cursive
10 POINT

1. Manufacturers of phototypesetting equipment furnish charts showing characters per pica in all type sizes and styles that the particular company has available. One of these charts is shown on page 100.

   Note: Helios Thin II 8-point has 3.3205 characters per pica, while 10-point type in the same family has 2.5900 characters per pica.

Typeface	6	8	10	12	14	18	24	30	36	48	60	72
Antique Olive	3.5972	2.7120	2.1405	1.8369	1.5191	1.2075	0.8885	0.7086	0.5567	0.3743	0.3108	0.2333
Antique Olive Bold	3.4079	2.5517	2.0078	1.5602	1.3387	1.1068	0.7848	0.6204	0.5195	0.3505	0.3000	0.2196
Antique Olive Compact	2.8619	2.1494	1.7209	1.4191	1.1773	0.9470	0.6916	0.5717	0.4357	0.3193	0.2227	0.1965
Antique Olive Medium	3.6624	2.6979	2.1405	1.7679	1.5102	1.1780	0.8355	0.6944	0.5551	0.3835	0.3000	0.2333
Benguiat Bold	3.4305	2.5643	2.0155	1.6602	1.4192	1.1092	0.8081	0.6574	0.5382	0.3727	0.3099	0.2196
Benguiat Bold Italic	3.4079	2.5517	2.0394	1.6550	1.4192	1.1068	0.7837	0.6411	0.5375	0.3727	0.3000	0.2196
Cartier	4.933	3.6738	3.0116	2.4785	2.1405	1.6550	1.2103	0.9867	0.7853	0.5736	0.4364	0.3394
Cartier Italic	6.3951	4.7963	3.8370	3.1975	2.6564	2.1229	1.5793	1.2665	1.0537	0.6901	0.5333	0.4667
English Times (all)	4.6250	3.3205	2.6030	2.1405	1.8500	1.4674	1.1021	0.8633	0.6972	0.5077	0.3692	0.3111
Floridian Script	5.6304	4.2810	3.4079	2.9770	2.4550	1.8836	1.4716	1.1335	0.9419	0.6370	0.4800	0.3733
Friz Quadrata	3.6479	3.0471	2.3981	2.0000	1.6603	1.3351	0.9664	0.7920	0.6026	0.4690	0.3467	0.3111
Goudy Bold, Bold It and Handtooled	4.0469	3.0292	2.3871	2.0000	1.6984	1.3351	0.9664	0.7933	0.6311	0.4732	0.3429	0.2872
Goudy Extrabold	4.1774	3.1779	2.4785	2.0556	1.7267	1.3632	1.0000	0.8288	0.6532	0.4907	0.3429	0.3111
Helios II Italic	3.8947	2.9942	2.3439	1.9847	1.6603	1.3248	0.9470	0.7872	0.6026	0.4569	0.3200	0.2489
Helios SE Bold, Bld Outline	3.8657	2.8152	2.2232	1.8768	1.5988	1.2573	0.9104	0.7245	0.5695	0.4003	0.3200	0.2489
Helios SE Bold Italic	3.8370	2.8152	2.3229	1.8836	1.6037	1.2573	0.9104	0.7245	0.5695	0.4003	0.3200	0.2489
Helios Thin II	4.4274	3.3205	2.5900	2.2043	1.8369	1.4674	1.0680	0.8706	0.6907	0.4953	0.3692	0.3111
Helios Thin Italic II	4.4274	3.3205	2.5771	2.1674	1.8112	1.4469	1.0769	0.8691	0.6895	0.4953	0.3692	0.3111
Korinna Extrabold	3.6738	2.7553	2.2232	1.8049	1.5697	1.2047	0.8885	0.7184	0.5677	0.3997	0.3200	0.2333
Korinna Kursiv Extrabold	3.6224	2.6979	2.1317	1.8049	1.5371	1.2047	0.8633	0.7175	0.5669	0.3891	0.3000	0.2333
Mallard	4.2114	3.1975	2.4785	2.0637	1.7619	1.3813	1.0078	0.8288	0.6532	0.4907	0.3692	0.3111
Mallard Bold	4.1111	3.0833	2.4785	2.0078	1.7209	1.3420	0.9664	0.8288	0.6409	0.4818	0.3692	0.3111
Mallard Italic	4.2114	3.1975	2.5146	2.0637	1.7619	1.3813	1.0507	0.8288	0.6532	0.4907	0.3692	0.3111
Oracle, O. Bold, O. Italic	4.3529	3.2785	2.5517	2.1317	1.8112	1.4192	1.0571	0.8492	0.6807	0.4953	0.3692	0.3111
Paladium, P. Italic, P. Semibold	4.4274	3.3205	2.5771	2.1405	1.8112	1.4321	1.0975	0.8633	0.6972	0.5067	0.3692	0.3111
Park Avenue	5.3958	4.0469	3.2579	2.6161	2.2232	1.7441	1.3351	1.0680	0.8594	0.6192	0.4800	0.3733
Piranesi Italic	5.7556	4.7091	3.6738	3.1205	2.5900	2.0720	1.5280	1.1116	0.9764	0.6658	0.5333	0.4667
Quill	6.8518	5.0784	3.9846	3.3636	2.8152	2.2424	1.6818	1.3114	1.0843	0.7794	0.6000	0.4667
Sabon	3.7536	2.8000	2.2137	1.8434	1.5556	1.2304	0,8900	0.7316	0.5792	0.4330	0.3200	0.2489
Sabon Italic	4.4274	3.3205	2.6030	2.1405	1.8500	1.4270	1.0928	0.8662	0.6972	0.5077	0.3692	0.3111
Thunderbird Extracondensed	7.0000	5.3402	4.2459	3.5000	3.0650	2.3333	1.5988	1.4114	1.1512	1.0688	0.6000	0.4667
Univers 47 and 48	6.0233	4.5043	3.6479	3.0292	2.5517	2.0156	1.4633	1.7713	0.9419	0.6625	0.4800	0.4148
Univers 49	9.2500	6.8158	5.6923	4.6667	3.9846	3.1018	2.3229	1.8304	1.5287	1.0996	0.0800	0.5333
Univers 55	4.4274	3.3205	2.6030	2.1949	1.8500	1.4716	1.1021	0.8262	0.7051	0.5077	0.3763	0.3111
Univers 56	4.4274	3.3205	2.5900	2.2043	1.8434	1.5102	1.0928	0.8840	0.7038	0.5067	0.3692	0.3111
Univers 75	4.0469	3.0292	2.3333	2.0000	1.6603	1.3351	0.9593	0.7945	0.6026	0.4569	0.3467	0.3111
Univers 76	4.0155	3.0116	2.3333	1.9923	1.6444	1.2982	0.9557	0.7933	0.6026	0.4569	0.3429	0.3111
Univers 83	3.2174	2.4093	1.9257	1.5841	1.3114	1.0571	0.7731	0.6044	0.4758	0.3496	0.2526	0.2074
Venetian Script	6.5570	4.9333	3.8370	3.2785	2.6564	2.1765	1.5890	1.2634	1.0537	0.6919	0.5333	0.4667

2. Another method, called *alpha length,* involves actually setting the alphabet of the desired type in lowercase characters (a to z). Measure this in points and divide by 342.

abcdefghijklmnopqrstuvwxyz

abcdefghijklmnopqrstuvwxyz

3. Another method of determining characters per pica involves setting the type in the desired size and counting the characters in a 200-pica length.

characters per line

All of the EditWriter Series Operational components are designed to meet the most exacting needs of any composition department. Every effort has been made to make your operator comfortable and proficient with the EditWriter capabilities.

45
46
49
47

The keyboard is logically arranged. Common operational functions are grouped to provide fingertip control over input, proofing and correcting, formatting, word management and the final output.

42
44
50
47

Research and experience produced this efficient composition management keyboard, to shorten training, reduce errors, increase productivity and minimize operator fatigue. For example, single keystroke functions have been optimized for increased operational efficiency.

47
43
50
46
47

The Editing Keypad provides full cursor control and virtual scrolling of up to 200 lines of copy or 6,000 characters, more than three pages of copy for the average six inch by nine inch book.

51
53
49

As you can see, the EditWriter 7500 or 7700 composition functions are separate, distinct and easily identified. On this keyboard a competent typist learns operation and input quickly, to start producing composition.

48
52
47
52

955

Choose 20 full lines...
total characters 955 ÷ 20 =
average characters per line 47.75

Average characters per line
47.75 ÷ picas per line 20 =
Characters per pica 2.3875

Count the characters in each line, total, divide by the number of lines, and then divide by the number of picas in each line. This gives the average number of characters per pica in this type size and style only.

This method would have to be done for each size and each of the families of type available.

Determining the Number of Lines Needed

To determine the number of lines needed, find the characters in 1 line and divide by the total number of characters

Examples

1. Find the lines needed for a manuscript of 3560 characters set in 10-point Helios II Italic, 21 picas wide.

   According to the chart, 10-point Helios II Italic sets 2.3439 characters per pica.

   Characters per line = 21 × 2.3439 = 49.2219 characters
   = 49 characters (always round down to the full number of characters)
   Lines needed = 3560 ÷ 49 = 72+, or 73 lines

Determining the Depth the Manuscript Requires

It must first be determined if the manuscript will be set solid or will have leading. To determine the depth of copy, add the space needed for the type (number of lines times the size type) and the space needed for leading (number of points of leading times 1 less than the number of lines).

Example

1. Find the depth needed for 57 lines of Park Avenue set 10/12.

Space needed for type	= 57 × 10 =	570	
Space needed for leading	= 56 × 2 =	+112	
Total depth	=	682 points = 56 picas 10 points	

Determining the Number of Pages the Manuscript Requires

Use the following procedure to determine the number of pages needed for a manuscript.

1. Find the characters per line by multiplying the characters per pica times the pica width.

2. Find the lines needed by dividing the total characters to be printed by the characters per line (round up to next line).

3. Find the lines per page (check lines).

4. Find the number of pages needed by dividing the lines needed by the lines per page (round up to next page).

Example

1. Find the number of pages needed for a manuscript with 43,650 characters set in Korinna Kursiv 10/14, each page 45 × 60 picas.

    10-point Korinna Kursiv = 2.1317 characters per pica

    Characters per line = 45 × 2.1317 = 95.9265 = 95 characters

    Number of lines = 43,650 ÷ 95 = 459+ lines = 460 lines

    Points of depth available = 60 × 12 = 720 points available

    Lines per page = 720 ÷ 14 = 51+ lines = 51

    If 51 lines used . . . Space for type   = 51 × 10 =   510
    Space for leading = 50 × 4   = +200
    710 points

    If 52 lines used . . . Space for type   = 52 × 10 =   520
    Space for leading = 51 × 4   = +204
    724 points

    Use 51 lines per page.

    Number of pages needed = total lines 460 ÷ number of lines per page

    51 = 9+ or 10 pages

Determining the Copy Needed to Fit a Known Space

Use the following procedure to determine the amount of copy needed to fill a known space in a layout.

1. Find the number of characters per pica in the type size and style desired for the layout.

2. Determine the number of characters per line. Always round down the answer.

3. Determine the number of lines which will fit the space.

4. Determine the total number of characters by multiplying the characters per line times the number of lines that fit the space.

5. Determine the total words by dividing the total characters by 5 (the average number of letters per word).

Examples

1. Determine the amount of copy that will fit a space 24 × 32 picas using 10-point Helios II Italic set solid.

    10-point Helios II Italic yields 2.3439 characters per pica

    Characters per line = 24 × 2.3439 = 56.2536 = 56 characters

    Lines of copy = 32 × 12 ÷ 10 = 38+ lines = 38 lines

    Total characters = 38 × 56 = 2128 characters

    Words of copy = 2128 ÷ 5 = 425+ words = 425 words

Determining the Size Type to Use to Set a Given Manuscript to a Given Space

Use the following procedure to determine, after selection of a type style, the size type to use to fit a given manuscript to a given space.

1. Determine the number of characters in the manuscript.

2. Figure the number of lines that can fit in the allotted space using different point sizes and leading.

3. Find the total characters that fit on 1 line using this size type.

4. Check the chart for an appropriate size type.

<u>Examples</u>

1. What size Helios Thin II type should be used to fit a space of 25 × 35 picas with copy containing 2200 characters? Use 2 extra points of leading.

Using 6/8

Number of lines obtained using 6/8 = 35 × 12 ÷ 8 = 52+ = 52 lines
Characters per line using 6 point = 25 × 4.4274 = 110.685 = 110 characters
Characters in space = 110 × 52 = 5720 characters

Using 8/10

Number of lines obtained using 8/10 = 35 × 12 ÷ 10 = 42 lines
Characters per line using 8 point = 25 × 3.3205 = 83.0125 = 83 characters
Characters in space = 83 × 42 = 3486 characters

Using 10/12

Number of lines obtained using 10/12 = 35 × 12 ÷ 12 = 35 lines
Characters per line using 10 point = 25 × 2.5900 = 64.7500 = 64 characters
Characters in space = 64 × 35 = 2240 characters

Conclusion: The copy will be set in Helios Thin II 10/12.

PRACTICAL PROBLEMS

A. Find the number of characters in each of the following manuscripts.

   1.   _____

   Paper is packaged in several ways, depending on the quantity needed
and purchased. An understanding of these various package sizes will
enable you to purchase paper with more intelligence and convenience.

   The smallest is the package, and will contain from 100 to 250
sheets. The paper house may not break a package or, for that matter, any
sealed quantity of stock. You may find, from time to time, odd lots or
even a year end clearance that will make available to you small quantities of various stocks. This rarely happens, so be alert and buy stocks
that you may need occasionally, but may not need in large quantities.

   2.   _____

   The paper catalog is usually broken into some fifteen
parts. Thirteen of which describe the various paper grades
along with their prices per hundred weight (CWT). These
run the gamut of bond, bristol, through gummed label, ending up with cut papers. The two other parts -- supplies
and misc. schedules, will be discussed later. Let's cover
these thirteen categories now, step by step.

   3.   _____

   BOOK paper, the second major section, fills the need
through a variety of stocks for books, pamphlets, brochures,
manuals, etc. This section is split into two categories --
coated and uncoated stocks.

   The coated stocks range from coated one and two sides,
dull enamels, gloss, matte, kromekote to embossed enamel.
Coatings are made from clay plus other materials and are
applied by a blade or roller method to a base stock to
provide a smooth and sometimes glossy finish.

   The uncoated stocks consist of Alpine hi-bulk offset,
Mountie offset - smooth, vellum, or embossed, and Waylite
offset, just to mention a few of the brands available.
This categorie of stock may be interchanged with bonds
when the later is not available. A variety of forms and
other printing will utilize this type of stock.

4. _____

When paper is shipped into the plant, certain precautions will have to be observed. The Graphic Arts Technical foundation says: "If paper is unwrapped while cold and allowed to stand in the pressroom, it will quickly develop a bad case of waviness. This is because its low temperature chills the air immediately, surrounding the pile and raises the relative humidity to approximately the saturation point, or 100 per cent. Under these conditions, the edges of the sheet may pick up 10 to 12 per cent of moisture before the pile warms up. As the temperature of the pile rises this excess of moisture will be partially given off. In this process the moisture content of the paper at the edges will follow the desorption curve and will not return to the same moisture content as the rest of the sheet. While the waviness may be reduced somewhat, it will not disappear completely."

B. Determine the number of characters per pica for each of the following. Refer to the chart on page 100.

1. Antique Olive—10 point _____

2. Sabon Italic—6 point _____

3. Piranesi Italic—14 point _____

4. Helios Thin II—12 point _____

5. Use the third method discussed in this unit to determine the number of characters per pica for the following manuscript.

The photo unit of the EditWriter increases efficien- _____
cy by providing eight typefaces in twelve sizes on- _____
line — 96 different fonts from 6 to 72 point in the _____
High Range machine and 6 to 36 point in the Low _____
Range model. Area composition can be achieved _____
anywhere within the 45-pica line length and full _____
mixing of all type styles and sizes within the same _____
line. This means that tabular jobs, magazine ads _____
and display ads can emerge camera-ready directly _____
from the machine. The photo unit has been proven _____
through years of use as the photo unit in the Com- _____
pugraphic CompuWriter IV. Further, filmstrips and _____
other typographic accessories are interchangeable _____
between the EditWriter and CompuWriter IV. _____

Another EditWriter efficiency plus is that the photo _____
unit can output independent of the display word _____
management functions. This means that as one job _____
is input, proofed or corrected another job of up to _____
6,000 characters can be set by the photo unit. As _____
soon as a job is input. Your operator can store it on _____
disk or send it to the photo unit and immediately _____
continue operation. _____

All EditWriters use a full 54-unit character width _____
system to produce excellent character fit. Kerning _____
as well as character compensation may be controll- _____
ed to one ninth of a point, resulting in high. . . _____

C. Find the number of lines needed for the following manuscripts.

1. 5670 characters, set 8-point Korinna Extrabold, set 18 picas wide. _____

2. 9535 characters, set 10-point Antique Olive, set 24 picas wide. _____

3. 20,580 characters, set 10-point English Times, set 25 picas wide. _____

4. 45,650 characters, set 12-point Univers 55, set 28 picas wide. _____

5. 19,385 characters set 8-point English Times, set 45 picas wide. _____

D. Find the depth needed for the following copy.

    1. 65 lines set 8-point solid. _____

    2. 83 lines set 8/10. _____

    3. 2630 characters set 12-point Mallard, set 25 picas wide with no leading. _____

    4. 3350 characters set Korinna Extrabold 10/12, set 28 picas wide. _____

    5. 4675 characters set Oracle 8/10, set 45 picas wide. _____

E. Determine the number of pages needed for each of the following manuscripts.

    1. 20,675 characters set 10-point Helios Thin II, each page 28 × 45 picas. _____

    2. 57,375 characters set Mallard 10/12, each page 45 × 60 picas. _____

    3. 125,640 characters set Paladium 10/14, each page 45 × 60 picas. _____

    4. 6375 characters set Univers 55 8/10, each page 25 × 35 picas. _____

    5. 10,350 characters set English Times 10/12, each page 25 × 35 picas. _____

F. Find the number of words of copy that will fit each of the following spaces.

    1. 35 × 40 picas set 8-point solid Oracle. _____

    2. 24 × 33 picas set 10-point solid Helios Thin Italic II. _____

    3. 18 × 26 picas set Antique Olive Compact, 8/10. _____

    4. 25 × 35 picas set Goudy Bold 10/12. _____

    5. 45 × 60 picas set Friz Quadrata, 10/14. _____

G. Find the size type which will be used to fit the given copy to the given space. Use 2 extra points of leading for each problem.

    1. 2560 characters, set in Korinna Extrabold, 25 × 35 picas. _____

    2. 3570 characters, set Helios Thin II, 28 × 45 picas. _____

    3. 4375 characters, set Mallard, 24 × 30 picas. _____

    4. 6375 characters, set Korinna Kursiv Extrabold, 45 × 60 picas. _____

    5. 2540 characters, set Helios Thin Italic II, 25 × 38 picas. _____

Unit 28 COST OF COMPOSITION

Basic Principles

- Apply the principles of determining the cost of composition by solving the practical problems in this unit.

Pricing by the Number of Characters

To price by the number of characters in the copy, determine the number of characters and divide this number by 1000, multiply by the price per 1000 characters of machine quality, and add any extra charges for quality type. This text uses $4.45 as the price per 1000 characters of machine quality.

$$\text{Cost} = \frac{\text{number of characters}}{1000} \times \text{price per 1000 characters}$$

$$+ \text{ any extra charges for quality type}$$

Extra charges—add to *machine quality* type charges to make:

Medium Quality 25%
Excellent Quality 75%
Tabular Matter* 100%
Ad or Display Type* 100%
*Deduct 10% for any preformatted material

Examples

1. Using the character method, what is the cost for a manuscript containing 45,650 characters set machine quality?

$$\text{Cost} = \frac{45,650}{1000} \times 4.45 = \$203.14$$

2. Using the character method, what is the cost for a manuscript set in 10-point Helios II Italic, medium quality, fit in a space 24 × 35 picas?

   10-point Helios II Italic yields 2.3439 characters per pica

   Characters per line = 24 × 2.3439 = 56.2536 = 56 characters

   Lines of copy = 35 × 12 ÷ 10 = 42 lines

   Total characters = 56 × 42 = 2352 characters

$$\text{Cost} = \frac{2352}{1000} \times 4.45 = 10.47 + (25\% \times 10.47) = 10.47 + 2.62 = \$13.08$$

Pricing by the Em Method

To price by the em method, determine the number of ems in the copy and divide this number by 100, multiply by the price per 100 ems, and then add any extra charges for quality type. Use the table below and the table on page 109.

$$\text{Cost} = \frac{\text{Total ems}}{100} \times \text{charge per 100 em} +$$
$$+ \text{ any extra charges for quality type}$$

Rate per 100 ems of Type (machine quality)

6 point	$1.92
8 point	1.45
10 point	1.15
12 point	.97

Examples

1. Using the em method, find the cost of setting a piece of copy containing 4,650 ems in 8-point machine quality type.

$$\text{Cost} = \frac{4650}{100} \times 1.45 = \$67.43$$

2. A customer orders an ad that has been preformatted. The ad is 24 × 24 picas set 12/16. Using the em method, what is the cost for this ad?

Ems per line = 24 × 12 ÷ 12 = 24 ems
Number of lines = 24 × 12 ÷ 16 = 18 lines
Ems in ad = 24 × 18 = 432 ems

$$\text{Cost} = \frac{432}{100} \times .97 = 4.19 + 90\% \text{ for preformatted ad}$$
$$= \$4.19 + 3.77 = \$7.96$$

Pricing by the Square Inch Method

To price by the square inch method, find the area of the type (length × width), multiply by the square inch rate, subtract the deduction for leading, and add any extra charges for quality type. The tables below give the square inch rate and the deductions for leading.

Cost = square inches × charge per square inch − leading deduction + any extra charges for quality type

Square Inch Rate (machine quality)

6 point	$2.76
8 point	1.18
10 point	.60
12 point	.35

Deductions for Leading

Leading	6 point	8 point	10 point	12 point
1 point	− 15%	− 12%	− 9%	− 8%
2 point	− 25%	− 20%	− 17%	− 15%

Examples

1. Using the square inch method, find the cost of composition for copy 3″ × 5″ set 8-point medium quality.

Cost = (3 × 5) × 1.18 =   17.70
          + 25% for quality   + 4.43
                                            $22.13

2. A booklet contains 18 pages of 24 × 32 picas and is set in excellent quality 10/12 type. What is the cost of composition using the square inch method?

Area = $\frac{24}{6} \times \frac{32}{6}$ = 21 1/3 square inches per page

Total area in booklet = 21 1/3 × 18 = 384 sq in

Cost = 384 × .60 = $230.40
          Less 17% for leading   –   39.17
                                                        $191.23
          Plus 75% for quality   + 143.42
                                                        $334.65

PRACTICAL PROBLEMS

A. Using the character method, find the cost of composition in each of the following problems.

1. What is the cost of a manuscript containing 25,650 characters set machine quality?   _____

2. A manuscript contains 4675 characters: What is the cost of this manuscript set excellent quality?   _____

3. A display ad set in Antique Olive Bold measures 45 picas wide by 60 picas deep. The ad contains 20 lines of 18-point type (1.1068 characters per pica) and 4 lines of 30-point type (.6204 characters per pica). What is the cost?   _____

4. Find the cost of copy 18 picas wide by 24 picas deep set in 10-point English Times set 10/12, excellent quality.   _____

5. Find the cost of copy 12 picas wide by 30 picas deep set in Oracle 10/12. The copy is preformatted tabular material.   _____

B. Using the em method, find the cost of composition in each of the following problems.

1. Find the cost of a manuscript containing 45,675 ems set in 10-point type.   _____

2. What is the charge for a piece of copy containing 8325 ems set in 6-point type, excellent quality?   _____

3. A book will have 250 pages if set in 8/10 with a page size of 24 × 35 picas. What is the cost of composition, if the book is set excellent quality? _____

4. Find the cost of setting 10 pages, each 30 × 35 picas set 6/8 medium quality? _____

5. A book containing 46 pages, each 23 × 36 picas, is set 8/10 excellent quality. Find the cost of composition. _____

C. Using the square inch method, find the cost of composition in each of the following problems.

1. The type form for a job measures 7″ × 9″. If the job is set 6-point solid, machine quality, what is the cost of composition? _____

2. Find the cost of composition for a mailing card printed 3″ × 5″ set 8/10 medium quality. _____

3. An announcement measures 6″ × 10″. Find the cost of composition if set 12/13 excellent quality. _____

4. A 4-page booklet is to have the type on each page 9″ × 12″. What is the cost composition if set 6/8 medium quality? _____

5. A book contains 325 pages. The type on each page measures 45 × 60 picas. If set 10/11 excellent quality, what is the cost of composition? _____

6. A financial report containing 24 pages of tabular matter and 12 pages of excellent quality body copy will be sent out. The tabular matter will be set 8/9 and the body copy 10/12. The type on each page measures 5″ × 7″. What is the cost of composition? _____

7. A full tabloid auction bill has to be set. Type will cover 85% of the page. The outside borders of the ad are 61 1/2 × 88 1/2 picas. What is the cost of composition for this ad, if set 12/14? _____

Unit 29 PACKAGING PAPER

Basic Principles

- Apply the principles of packaging paper to the printing and graphic communications industry by solving the practical problems in this unit.

Paper is packaged in several ways, depending on the quantity needed and purchased. An understanding of these various package sizes enables the printer to purchase paper more conveniently and intelligently.

Packaging of Printing Papers

The following is a break down of the packaging of printing papers.

Broken Carton or Package: less than full factory-sealed package or carton.

Package: Stock wrapped in a paper covering and usually placed in a master carton. Bond paper is wrapped in lots of 500 sheets (ream), index paper is wrapped in lots of 100 sheets, and text and cover papers are wrapped in lots of 250 sheets.

Carton: Loose sheets that in total weigh approximately 125 pounds. The carton can also contain a number of wrapped packages. The loose stock has a marker every 500 sheets for ease in counting. The Roman numerals M (1000), D (500), and C (100) are used to identify the number of sheets in a package or carton.

Skid: Loose sheets overwrapped with a moistureproof wrapper strapped to a wooden platform. A skid weighs from 1500 pounds to 3000 pounds.

Bundle: Loose sheets, tied securely, that in total weigh approximately 50 pounds. Chipboard is the most common example of this type of packaging. The number of sheets in a bundle varies according to the thickness of the board. All board is packaged in bundles of 50 pounds each.

Cabinet: Stationery and envelopes or wedding invitations contained in a package or box suitable for display, reuse or for storage of the product. These cabinets may contain 50 to 100 items and will come in master cartons.

Box: Contains ream-wrapped cut paper, envelopes, and other items, for convenient use by the printer and for resale in small quantities to the customer. Items that are hard to wrap or otherwise inconvenient for the printer to obtain packaging for are available in boxes. Number 10 envelopes are packed 500 to the box and 2500 to the master carton, and number 6 3/4 envelopes are packed 500 to the box and 5000 to the master carton.

Examples

1. An order calls for 2500 sheets of bond paper. Determine the number of packages (reams) in this order.

    1 package or ream = 500 sheets
    2500 ÷ 500 = 5 reams

2. An order calls for 6000 sheets of cover stock. Determine the number of packages in the order.

    1 package = 250 sheets
    6000 ÷ 250 = 24 packages

3. An order calls for 5000 envelopes (no. 10's). Determine the number of boxes and master cartons in this order.

    1 box = 500 envelopes
    5000 ÷ 500 = 10 boxes
    1 master carton = 2500 envelopes
    5000 ÷ 2500 = 2 master cartons

4. An order calls for 3000 pounds of chipboard. Determine the number of bundles in the order.

    1 bundle = 50 pounds
    3000 ÷ 50 = 60 bundles

PRACTICAL PROBLEMS

1. An order calls for 5500 sheets of 17″ × 22″ bond paper. Determine the number of packages in the order. _____

2. An order calls for 500 pounds of bond paper. Determine the number of cartons in this order. _____

3. An order calls for 6000 pounds of chipboard. How many bundles are in the order? _____

4. An order calls for 5000 sheets of 20″ × 26″ cover paper. Determine the number of packages in the order. _____

5. An order calls for 2000 sheets of 20 1/2″ × 24 3/4″ index paper. Determine the number of packages in the order. _____

6. An order calls for 10,000 envelopes (no. 6 3/4's). Determine the number of boxes and master cartons in the order. _____

7. An order calls for 7500 pounds of chipboard. How many bundles are in the order? _____

8. An order calls for 80,000 sheets of 17″ × 22″ bond, 20 pounds per ream. Determine the number of reams and the number of 2000-pound skids in the order. _____

9. An order calls for 75,000 sheets of bond, 16 pounds per ream. How many reams are contained in the order? How many 1500-pound skids are contained in the order? _____

10. An order calls for 300 wedding invitations. How many cabinets, each containing 50 invitations, are in the order? _____

Unit 30 BASIC SIZE, THICKNESS, AND WEIGHT OF STOCK

Basic Principles

- Apply the principles of determining the basic size, thickness, and weight of stock to the printing and graphic communications industry by solving the practical problems in this unit.

Basic Size

Paper and paper stock are manufactured in a variety of sizes, weights, colors, and compositions. Paper stock may be ordered in many different sizes, but all stock is classified into basic sizes and weights. The basic sizes of the various types of paper and paper stock are shown below.

Bond and Ledgers Writings, Mimeograph, Duplicator, Gummed, Flats	17 × 22	Card Stock Rope, Bogus, Tag, Folding, Postcard Ticket, Wedding	24 × 36
Blotting Papers Plain, Coated	19 × 24	Cover papers Speciality covers	20 × 26
Blanks Translucents, Railroad, Tough check, Poster, Calendar, Sign Board, Playing Card	22 × 28	Manilas Poster, Kraft	24 × 36
		Newsprint Poster paper	24 × 36
Board Binders, Cloth Corrugated	20 × 30	Padding board Strawboard, Chipboard, Boxboard	26 × 38
Book papers Offset, Label, Text, Ballot, Coated, Uncoated	25 × 38	Pressboard Tagboard	24 × 36
		*Thin papers Manifold, Onion skin, Tissues, Parchment	17 × 22
Bristols Mill Index	25 1/2 × 30 1/2	Tympan papers (.006) in rolls 15″–70″ widths and cut in sizes for most presses	24 × 36
Carbon papers Pencil, Typewriter, Copying (Hectograph) One side, both sides	22 × 34	*Wrappings Manila, White Specialty	24 × 36

*Comes cut in sheets, 480 sheets to the package, and in rolls of various widths and weights. Other trade sizes are available in these papers but are usually multiples of those listed.

Thickness

The *ply* is the standard unit of thickness for measuring paper or board. A ply is measured in points, each equaling .001 inch. As the number of plys increases, the number of points increases. Thus, 24-point paper is .024 inch thick.

Approximate Calipers per Single Sheet (1 Point Equals 1/1000 of an Inch)

Bond
Basis 17 × 22
20/40M . . . . 4 points

Ledger
Basis 17 × 22
28/56M . . . . 5 points

Manifold
Basis 17 × 22
9/18M . . . . 1 1/2 points

Book Basis 25 × 38
Coated Book
60/120 . . . . 3 points

Eggshell Book
60/120M . . . . 6 points

English Finish Book
60/120M . . . . 4 points

Plain Offset
60/120M . . . . 4 1/2 points

Cover
Basis 20 × 26
Plain Cover
65/130M . . . . 9 1/2 points

Coated Cover
60/120M . . . . 5 1/2 points

Bristol
Index Bristol
Basis 25 1/2 × 30 1/2
110/220M . . . . 8 1/4 points

Printing Bristols
Basis 22 1/2 × 28 1/2
100/200M Plate . . . . 8 1/2 points
100/200M Antique . . . . 11 points

Blank, Railroad Board
4 ply . . . . 18 points

Tagboard
Basis 24 × 36
100/200M . . . . 8 points

This chart contains a token amount of the entries found in charts in the Paper Catalog.

Examples

1. A book contains 450 pages. How thick is the book if 3 1/2-point paper is used?

   450 pages takes 225 sheets of paper
   225 × .0035 = .7875 inch thick

2. Four sheets of a 60-pound paper caliper 16 points. How thick in inches is 248 pages?

   If 4 sheets caliper 16 points, then 1 sheet is .016 ÷ 4 = .004 inch
   248 pages takes 124 sheets of paper
   124 × .004 = .496 inch thick

Blanks are also sold by the ply. The following is a formula that relates ply numbers and thickness of blanks. This formula applies only to blanks and not to other bonds or bristols which have their weight described in terms of ply.

3 × ply number + 6 = thickness in points

Examples

1. What is the thickness of a 4-ply blank?

    $(3 \times 4) + 6 = 18$ points or .018"

2. A customer wants a blank to caliper 36 points. What ply blank must be purchased?

    $(3 \times \text{ply}) + 6 = 36$ points
    $3 \times \text{ply} = 30$ points
    $3 \times 10 = 30$ points, blank must be 10 ply

Basic Weight of Paper

Basic sizes of paper have basic weights. The weight of a ream of paper is designated by a substance number (in pounds) and/or the actual weight of 1 ream (500 sheets) of the paper. When paper is listed $17 \times 22 - 20$ this means that the size of the paper is 17" $\times$ 22", and the weight of 1 ream is 20 pounds.

$17 \times 22 - 20$ is read as 17×22 substance 20, or as 17×22 Basis 20, and may be written in any one of the following ways:

$17 \times 22 - 20$
$17 \times 22 - $ Sub. 20
$17 \times 22 - 20D$
$17 \times 22 - 40M(S20)$
$17 \times 22 - 40M$
$17 \times 22 - $ Basis 20

Grain

The direction of the grain of the paper is indicated on the end label in 1 of 2 ways. The direction of the grain is either underlined in the dimensions, or marked short grain or long grain.

Examples

1.

$17 \times \underline{22} - 16$ Substance 16 D16 lb M32 lb	Name Brand BOND PAPER	WHITE One Ream 500 Sheets

The substance number is 16, and the grain is long.

2.

25 × 38	Name Brand	WHITE
		One Ream
Substance 60	BOOK PAPER	500 Sheets

The substance number is 60, and the grain is short.

PRACTICAL PROBLEMS

A. Answer each of the following.

1. What is the basic size for bond and writing paper? _____

2. What is the basic size for book paper? _____

3. What is the basic size for cover paper? _____

4. What is the basic size for card stock? _____

5. What is the standard unit of thickness, and in what unit is thickness measured? _____

6. If 2 plys of card stock are .012 inch thick, and each additional ply is .003 inch, determine the number of points in 5 plys. _____

7. A book contains 250 pages. How thick is the book if 4-point paper is used? _____

8. Six sheets of a 60-pound paper caliper 24 points. How thick in inches is 246 pages? _____

9. A printer has a stack of 60-pound stock 3 inches thick. If this stack contains 750 sheets, what point size is the 60-pound stock? _____

10. A book contains 150 pages. How thick is the book if 3 1/2-point paper is used? _____

11. A customer's case binding is limited to 1 3/8 inches. A 560-page book must be within the 1 3/8 inches. What must the average caliper of each sheet be? _____

12. Four sheets of a 50-pound caliper 14 points. How thick in inches is 248 pages? _____

13. Four sheets of a 70-pound caliper 18 points. How thick in inches is 248 pages? _____

14. Four sheets of a 60-pound caliper 16 points. How thick in inches is 244 pages? _____

15. A customer's case binding is limited to 1 5/8 inches. A 540-page book must be within that 1 5/8 inches. What must the average caliper of each sheet be?

    _____

16. A customer's case binding is limited to 2 1/8 inches. A 620-page book must be within that 2 1/8 inches. What must the average caliper of each sheet be?

B. Give the substance number and the direction of the grain in each of the following.

1.

    _____

BRAND NAME INDEX	22 1/2 × 35–222M 572 × 889 mm 600 Sheets GRAIN LONG ITEM CODE 23097	B 110 a 199 g/m² g s GREEN

2.

    _____

4024 Dual Purpose   8 1/2 × <u>11</u>   **BRAND**
Reorder:
    10 ream Carton

500 sheets, 8 1/2 × 11 Substance 20
White   3R721
      , N.Y.   Printed in U.S.A.

3.

    _____

NAME BRAND ADDRESS USA	NAME BOND 8 1/2 × 11–5 10M 216 × 279 mm Grain Long 500 Shts	 Sub 20 75 g/m² Blue

4.

    _____

NAME INDEX

	Boxes	Grain	No. of Sheets	
22 1/2 × 35–222M	110	Long	600	Item
572 mm 889 mm	199 g/m²			3388

5. _____

BRAND Opaque Cover Vellum

NAME   23 × 35–100 1/2   201M   Bs. 65

ADDRESS   584 × 889 mm   176 g/m²

Citrus Yellow   750 Shts   455-1401

6. _____

0638

NAME BRAND BOND   8 1/2 × 11 − 10M

Sub. 20

White

5000 sheets

Unit 31 EQUIVALENT WEIGHTS

BASIC PRINCIPLES

- Apply the principles of determining equivalent weights to the printing and graphic communications industry by solving the practical problems in this unit.

When paper is listed 25 × 38 − 60, this means that the dimension of the paper is 25″ × 38″ and that 1 ream (500 sheets) weighs 60 pounds. Such paper is referred to as *60-pound paper*. Sixty-pound paper that measures 50″ × 38″ weighs 120 pounds per ream. Different sizes of paper in the same basis category are of different weights. Printer's catalogs list the weights for the different sizes of the basic size paper. If a catalog is not available, the square inch method or the paper dealers' method can be used to calculate the weight.

Square Inch Method

The square inch method is used to calculate the weight of 1 ream (500 sheets). This method does not require the use of a chart.

To find the weight of a ream of paper using the square inch method, find the weight per square inch in a ream the basic size by dividing the basic weight by the area of the basic size. The answer is then multiplied by the area of the desired size.

<u>Examples</u>

1. What is the equivalent weight of a ream of 17″ × 28″ paper for a 20-pound bond?

   $$\frac{20 \text{ (basic weight)}}{17 \times 22 \text{ (area of basic size)}} \times 17 \times 28 \text{ (area of desired size)}$$

   $$\frac{20}{374} \times 476 = \frac{9520}{374} = 25.5 \text{ lb (500 sheets)}$$

2. Find the 1000-sheet weight for 32 1/4″ × 43 3/4″, coated offset in the basic size 25 × 38 - 120M.

   $$\frac{120 \text{ (basic weight per M)}}{25 \times 38 \text{ (area of basic size)}} \times 32 \text{ }1/4 \times 43 \text{ }3/4 \text{ (area of desired size)}$$

   $$\frac{120}{950} \times 1410 \text{ }15/16 = \frac{169,312 \text{ }1/2}{950} = 178 \text{ M}$$

Paper Dealers' Method

The paper dealers' method is also used to find the equivalent weight of stock. The decimal weight factors for bond, book, and cover papers are given in the table on page 123. The *decimal weight factor* is the weight per square inch of 1000 sheets of paper.

BOND and LEDGER PAPERS		17 × 22 Basis		(374 sq in)		1000 Sheets			
Basis Weight	16	20	24	28	32	36	40	44	49	51
DSN (1 M)	.086	.107	.128	.150	.171	.193	.214	.236	.262	.272

BOOK PAPERS		25 × 38 Basis		(950 sq in)		1000 Sheets			
Basis Weight	30	35	40	45	50	60	70	80	100	120
DSN (1 M)	.063	.074	.084	.095	.105	.126	.147	.168	.210	.252

COVER PAPERS		20 × 26 Basis		(520 sq in)		1000 Sheets			
Basis Weight	25	35	40	50	65	80	90	100	130	160
DSN (1 M)	.096	.134	.154	.192	.250	.308	.346	.384	.500	.616

To find the equivalent weight of 1000 sheets, multiply the area of the desired size by the decimal weight factor. Round all answers to the nearest 1/2 pound.

Examples

1. What is the equivalent weight of 1000 sheets of 19″ × 24″ bond, substance 16?

   The basic weight factor for 16-pound bond is .086.
   19″ × 24″ (area of desired size) × .086 = 456 × .086
   $$= 39 \text{ lb per 1000 sheets}$$

2. Find the equivalent weight of 1000 sheets of 24″ × 38″, substance 60 book.

   The basic weight factor for a 60-pound book is .126.
   24″ × 38″ (area of desired size) × .126 = 912 × .126
   $$= 115 \text{ lb per 1000 sheets}$$

3. Determine the equivalent weight of a ream of 25 1/2″ × 30 1/2″, substance 20 bond.

   The basic weight factor for a 20-pound bond is .107.
   25 1/2″ × 30 1/2″ (area of desired size) × .107 = 777.75 × .107
   $$= 83 \text{ lb per 1000 sheets}$$

   83 ÷ 2 = 42 lb per ream

PRACTICAL PROBLEMS

A. Solve each of the following problems using the square inch method.

1. Determine the weight of a ream of paper measuring 35″ × 45″ if the basic ream is 25″ × 38″ and weighs 70 pounds.   _____

2. Determine the weight of a ream of paper measuring 22 1/2″ × 28 1/2″ if the basic ream is 20″ × 26″ – 65.   _____

3. Determine the weight of a ream of paper measuring 28″ × 34″ if the basic ream weighs 28 pounds and is 17″ × 22″.   _____

4. Determine the weight of a ream of paper measuring 17″ × 28″ if the basic ream weighs 16 pounds and is 17″ × 22″.   _____

5. Determine the weight of a ream of paper measuring 19″ × 24″ if the basic ream weighs 20 pounds and is 17″ × 22″.   _____

6. A ream of paper measuring 25″ × 38″ weighs 80 pounds. What does a ream 35″ × 45″ of the same grade weigh?   _____

7. Determine the weight of a ream of paper measuring 24″ × 36″ if the basic ream is 25″ × 38″ and weighs 60 pounds.   _____

8. A basic ream measuring 25″ × 38″ weighs 70 pounds. What is the weight of 2000 sheets of paper measuring 17″ × 28″ if the basic size ream is 17″ × 22″ and weighs 40 pounds?   _____

9. Determine the weight of 5000 sheets of book measuring 35″ × 45″ if the basic weight is 80 pounds.   _____

10. Determine the weight of 3000 sheets of bond measuring 28″ × 34″ if the basic weight is 20 pounds.   _____

B. Solve each of the following problems using the paper dealers' method.

1. Determine the weight of 1000 sheets of paper measuring 32″ × 44″ if the basic ream is 25″ × 38″ – 60.   _____

2. Determine the weight of 1000 sheets of paper measuring 35″ × 45″ if the basic ream is 25″ × 38″ and weighs 70 pounds.   _____

3. Determine the weight of 1000 sheets of paper measuring 22 1/2″ × 28 1/2″ if the basic ream is 20″ × 26″ – 65.   _____

4. Determine the weight of 1000 sheets of paper measuring 28″ × 34″ if the basic ream weighs 28 pounds and is 17″ × 22″.   _____

5. Determine the weight of 1000 sheets of paper measuring 17″ × 28″ if the basic ream weighs 16 pounds and is 17″ × 22″. _____

6. Determine the weight of 1000 sheets of paper measuring 19″ × 24″ if the basic ream weighs 20 pounds and is 17″ × 22″. _____

7. If 1000 sheets of paper measuring 25″ × 38″ weigh 80 pounds, how much does a ream 35″ × 45″ of the same grade weigh? _____

8. Determine the weight of 3000 sheets of paper measuring 24″ × 36″ if the basic ream is 25″ × 38″ and weighs 60 pounds. _____

9. If the weight of a ream measuring 25″ × 38″ is 70 pounds, what is the weight of a ream measuring 42″ × 58″? _____

10. If a ream of paper measuring 17″ × 22″ weighs 20 pounds, find the weight of a ream of the same kind of paper measuring 22″ × 34″. _____

Unit 32 FIGURING AND CUTTING PAPER

Basic Principles

- Apply the principles of figuring and cutting paper to the printing and graphic communications industry by solving the practical problems in this unit.

Cutting, Stock When the Direction of Grain is an Important Factor

A printer must decide if the paper needed for a job should be cut with the grain, across the grain, or if the direction of the grain does not matter.

The grain of paper is important in the printing of a job as well as in the final use of a job. Paper folds more easily with the grain, and books fold with ease and stay open when the grain runs "up and down" the page. Cardboard posters stand without sagging when the grain runs up and down. Offset printing often requires that the grain run across the cylinder for color fit. Therefore, the direction of the grain should always be considered when planning the cutting of paper stock.

<u>Examples</u>

1. How many pieces 5″ × <u>3″</u> can be cut from a sheet of stock 17″ × <u>22″</u> if the grain must be up and down?

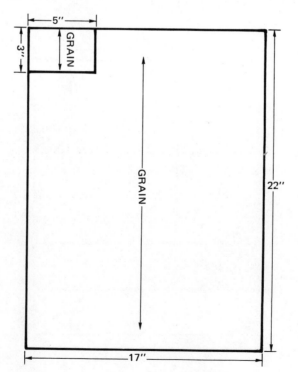

Divide the width of the stock by the width of the piece.

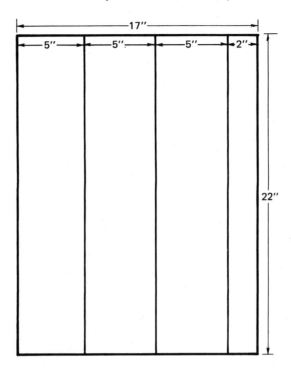

17 ÷ 5 = 3 with 2″ waste along the side
Divide the length of the stock by the length of the piece.

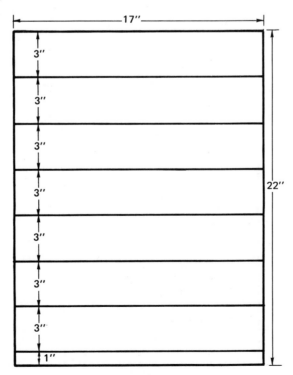

22 ÷ 3 = 7 with 1″ waste
Number of pieces is 3 × 7 = 21 pieces

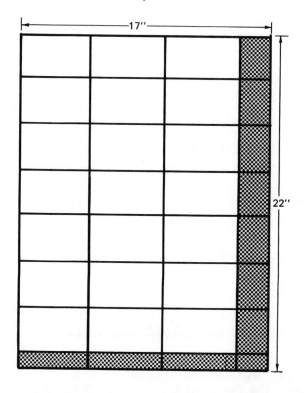

2. How many pieces 6″ × <u>9</u>″ can be cut from a sheet of stock 25″ × <u>38</u>″ if the grain must be up and down?

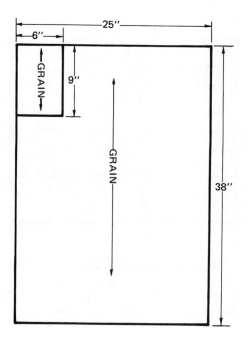

Divide the length of the stock by the length of the piece.

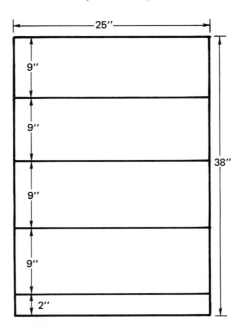

38 ÷ 9 = 4 with 2″ waste
Divide the width of the stock by the width of the piece.

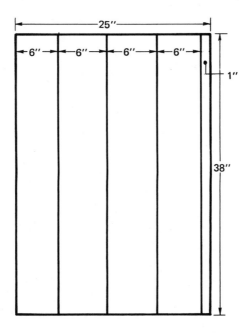

25 ÷ 6 = 4 with 1″ waste
Number of pieces is 4 × 4 = 16 pieces

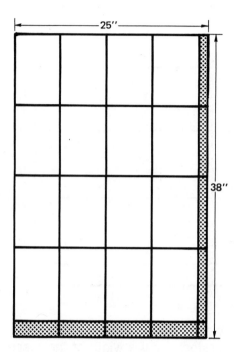

Cutting Stock When the Direction of Grain is not an Important Factor

When the direction of the grain is not an important factor, the printer figures the best cut and chooses the way in which the most pieces will be obtained. Fractional pieces become waste.

Examples

1. How many pieces 5″ × 3″ can be cut from a sheet of stock 19″ × 25″? Cut either with the grain or across the grain. Waste is not considered in this solution.

With grain

$$\frac{\overset{3}{19} \times \overset{8}{25}}{\underset{5}{\cancel{5}} \times \underset{3}{\cancel{3}}} = 3 \times 8 = 24 \text{ pieces}$$

Across the grain

$$\frac{\overset{6}{19} \times \overset{5}{25}}{\underset{5}{\cancel{5}} \times \underset{3}{\cancel{3}}} = 6 \times 5 = 30 \text{ pieces}$$

30 pieces is the more economical cut

2. How many pieces 5″ × 7″ can be cut from a sheet of stock 23″ × <u>29″</u>? Cut either with the grain or across the grain.

With grain

$$\frac{\overset{4}{23} \times \overset{4}{29}}{5 \times 7} = 4 \times 4 = 16 \text{ pieces}$$

Across the grain

$$\frac{\overset{3}{23} \times \overset{5}{29}}{5 \times 7} = 3 \times 5 = 15 \text{ pieces}$$

16 pieces is the more economical cut

Cutting Using Waste

For some uses such as making scratch pads, paper with different grain directions may be used in the same job. In this case, waste may be used. The use of drawings when dealing with this type of cutting problem is an advantage to the beginner and is a perfectly accepted practice.

<u>Examples</u>

1. How many pieces 3″ × 5″, without regard to grain, can be cut from a sheet of stock 23″ × <u>29″</u>?

A. 23 ÷ 3 = 7 with 2″ waste

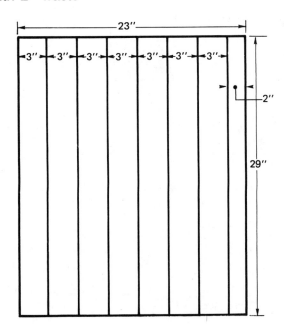

29 ÷ 5 = 5 with 4″ waste

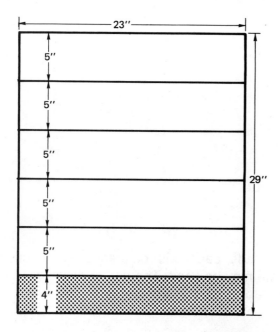

Number of pieces out of stock is 7 × 5 = 35 pieces

Out of waste

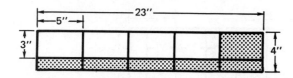

4 ÷ 3 = 1 with 1″ waste
23 ÷ 4 = 4 with 3″ waste

Number of pieces out of waste = 1 × 4 = 4 pieces
Total pieces out of stock = 35 + 4 = 39 pieces

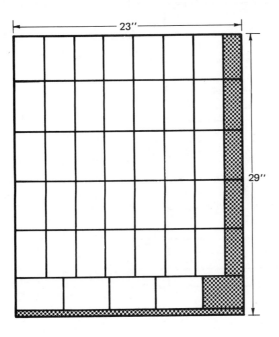

B. 23 ÷ 5 = 4 with 3″ waste

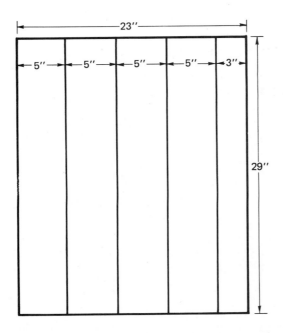

29 ÷ 3 = 9 with 2″ waste

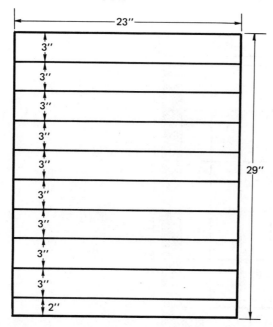

Number of pieces out of stock is 4 × 9 = 36 pieces
Out of waste

3 ÷ 3 = 1
29 ÷ 5 = 5 with 4″ waste

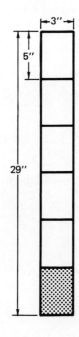

Number of pieces out of waste = 1 × 5 = 5 pieces
Total pieces out of stock = 36 + 5 = 41 pieces

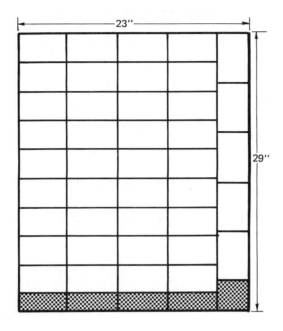

PRACTICAL PROBLEMS

A.   Calculate the number of pieces obtained from each sheet of stock in the following problems. Observe the grain direction.

1.   How many pieces 5″ × 3″ can be cut from a sheet of stock 22″ × 34″? _____

2.   How many pieces 2 1/2″ × 4 1/2″ can be cut from a sheet of stock 28″ × 34″? _____

3.   How many pieces 5″ × 7″ can be cut from a sheet of stock 24″ × 38″? _____

4.   How many pieces 12 1/2″ × 9 1/2″ can be cut from a sheet of stock 38″ × 50″? _____

5.   How many pieces 6″ × 9″ can be cut from a sheet of stock 17 1/2″ × 22 1/2″? _____

6.   How many pieces 4″ × 6″ can be cut from a sheet of stock 17″ × 22″? _____

7.   How many pieces 9″ × 11″ can be cut from a sheet of stock 35″ × 45″? _____

8.   How many pieces 3 1/2″ × 5 1/2″ can be cut from a sheet of stock 23″ × 35″? _____

9.   How many pieces 6″ × 9″ can be cut from a sheet of stock 25″ × 38″? _____

10. How many pieces 2 1/2″ × <u>4 3/4</u>″ can be cut from a sheet of stock 17 1/2″ × <u>22 1/2</u>″? _____

B. In each of the following problems, calculate the number of pieces and give the direction that the grain will be in the finished size. Cut either with the grain or across the grain. Waste should not be considered.

1. How many pieces 5″ × 3″ can be cut from a sheet of stock <u>26</u>″ × 40″? _____

2. How many pieces 4″ × 6″ can be cut from a sheet of stock 25″ × <u>38</u>″? _____

3. How many pieces 4 3/4″ × 2 1/2″ can be cut from a sheet of stock 18″ × <u>23</u>″? _____

4. How many pieces 12 3/4″ × 9 1/2″ can be cut from a sheet of stock 36″ × <u>48</u>″? _____

5. How many pieces 5″ × 3″ can be cut from a sheet of stock 24″ × <u>36</u>″? _____

6. How many pieces 5″ × 7″ can be cut from a sheet of stock 20″ × <u>40</u>″? _____

7. How many pieces 6″ × 9″ can be cut from a sheet of stock 38″ × <u>50</u>″? _____

8. How many pieces 3 1/2″ × <u>5 1/2</u>″ can be cut from a sheet of stock 23″ × <u>35</u>″? _____

9. How many pieces 6″ × 9″ can be cut from a sheet of stock 25″ × <u>38</u>″? _____

10. How many pieces 2 1/2″ × <u>4 3/4</u>″ can be cut from a sheet of stock 17 1/2″ × <u>22 1/2</u>″? _____

C. In each of the following problems, calculate the greatest number of pieces obtainable from a piece of stock.
Make use of the waste were possible.

1. How many pieces of 5″ × 3″ can be cut from a sheet of stock 17″ × <u>28</u>″? _____

2. How many pieces 2 1/2″ × 5″ can be cut from a sheet of stock <u>24</u>″ × 38″? _____

3. How many pieces 4″ × 6″ can be cut from a sheet of stock 17 1/2″ × <u>22 1/2</u>″? _____

4. How many pieces 1 1/2″ × 2 1/2″ can be cut from a sheet of stock 19″ × <u>24</u>″? _____

5. How many pieces 4″ × 5 1/2″ can be cut from a sheet of stock 36″ × <u>48</u>″? _____

Unit 33 FIGURING MOST ECONOMICAL CUT

Basic Principles

- Apply the principles of figuring the most economical cut to the printing and graphic communications industry by solving the practical problems in this unit.

Figuring the Most Economical Cut

The printer often has a choice of using different sizes of stock. It is advisable for the printer to use the size which uses the largest percentage of the stock.

To find the most economical cut, use the following procedure:
1. Calculate the number of pieces which can be obtained from the stock available.
2. Calculate the area available
3. Calculate the area actually used.
4. Calculate the percent used.
5. Choose the stock which uses the highest percentage.

<u>Examples</u>

1. Which of the following sheets of stock will cut pieces 5″ × <u>6</u>″ most economically (17″ × <u>22</u>″, 19″ × <u>24</u>″, <u>28</u>″ × 34″, observe grain direction)?

Number of pieces from each stock

$$\frac{17 \times 22}{5 \times 6} = 3 \times 3 = 9 \text{ pieces from the } 17″ \times 22″$$

$$\frac{19 \times 24}{5 \times 6} = 3 \times 4 = 12 \text{ pieces from the } 19″ \times 24″$$

$$\frac{28 \times 34}{5 \times 6} = 4 \times 6 = 24 \text{ pieces from the } 28″ \times 34″$$

Area available
17 × 22 = 374 sq in
19 × 24 = 456 sq in
28 × 34 = 952 sq in

Area actually used
from the 17 × 22 ----- 9 × 5 × 6 = 270 sq in
from the 19 × 24 ----- 12 × 5 × 6 = 360 sq in
from the 28 × 34 ----- 24 × 5 × 6 = 720 sq in

Percent actually used = area actually used ÷ total area
of the 17 × 22 ----- 270 ÷ 374 = .72 = 72%
of the 19 × 24 ----- 360 ÷ 456 = .79 = 79%
of the 28 × 34 ----- 720 ÷ 952 = .76 = 76%
Most economical cut ----- 19″ × 24″

PRACTICAL PROBLEMS

In each of the following, which sheet of stock will cut most economically? Observe the grain direction.

1. Pieces 3″ × 5″ from stock 17″ × <u>22</u>″, 17″ × <u>28</u>″, or 35″ × <u>45</u>″ _____

2. Pieces 4″ × 6″ from stock 19″ × <u>25</u>″, 23″ × <u>35</u>″, or 28″ × <u>44</u>″ _____

3. Pieces <u>5</u>″ × 7″ from stock 23″ × <u>29</u>″, <u>23</u>″ × 35″, or <u>26</u>″ × 40″ _____

4. Pieces 6″ × 9″ from stock 20″ × <u>26</u>″, <u>23</u>″ × 35″, or 35″ × <u>46</u>″ _____

5. Pieces 5″ × <u>8</u>″ from stock 22 1/2″ × <u>28 1/2</u>″, <u>22 1/2</u>″ × 28 1/2″, or 24″ × <u>36</u>″ _____

6. Pieces <u>8 1/2</u>″ × 11″ from stock 17″ × <u>22</u>″, 17″ × <u>28</u>″, or 19″ × <u>24</u>″ _____

7. Pieces 7 1/2″ × <u>10 1/2</u>″ from stock 19″ × <u>25</u>″, 23″ × <u>35</u>″, or 35″ × <u>45</u>″ _____

8. Pieces 3″ × 5″ from stock 25″ × <u>38</u>″, <u>20</u>″ × 26″, or 38″ × <u>50</u>″ _____

9. Pieces 7″ × <u>10</u>″ from stock 19″ × <u>25</u>″, 35″ × <u>45</u>″, or 38″ × <u>50</u>″ _____

10. Pieces 6″ × <u>4</u>″ from stock 20″ × <u>26</u>″, 23″ × <u>35</u>″, or 25″ × <u>38</u>″ _____

Unit 34 DETERMINING NUMBER OF SHEETS REQUIRED

BASIC PRINCIPLES

- Apply the principles of determining the number of sheets required for a job to the printing and graphic communications industry by solving the practical problems in this unit.

In figuring a job, the printer needs to calculate the number of sheets of stock to order for a job. Keep in mind that trade custom has established that overruns and underruns of 10% of the amount ordered constitutes an acceptable delivery unless otherwise stated by the customer or the printer.

The history of a plant's spoilage, which is affected by the skill of the workers and the condition of the equipment, must be taken into account when considering overrun. This text uses a 10% figure to cover spoilage and overrun/underrun.

To determine the exact amount of paper needed for any job, the number of pages in each signature must be known. A *signature* is a group of pages printed on 1 or 2 sides of a larger sheet that will be folded and become a part of a book, pamphlet, or other printed piece. Signatures may consist of 4 to 32 pages.

On all signatures of 4 or more pages, an allowance of at least 1/8 inch must be added on 3 sides of each page—fore edge, head, and tail (but not the binding edge). When folded, the printed signature may be trimmed 1/8 inch on each of these 3 edges so that the pages are of equal size in the finished book.

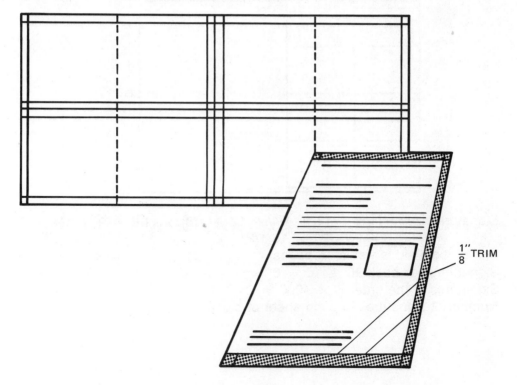

$\frac{1''}{8}$ TRIM

Calculating the Amount of Paper Needed

1. Figure the number of pieces obtained from a sheet of stock.

2. Divide the total press sheets needed for the job by the number obtained from a sheet of stock.

3. Add 10% to cover spoilage and overrun/underrun.

<u>Examples</u>

1. How many sheets of stock 17" × <u>22"</u> – 20 bond are needed for a job of 1200 letterheads 8 1/2" × <u>11"</u>?

   Number of pieces obtained from a sheet of stock

   $$\frac{\overset{2}{\cancel{17}} \times \overset{2}{\cancel{22}}}{\cancel{8\ 1/2} \times \cancel{11}} = 4 \text{ pieces from each sheet of stock } 17" \times 22"$$

   1200 ÷ 4 = 300 sheets of stock needed

   $$\begin{array}{r} 300 \\ +\ \ 30 \\ \hline 330 \end{array}$$ 10% of 300 for spoilage and overrun/underrun

   sheets of 17" × 22" needed for the job

2. How many sheets of stock 25" × <u>38"</u> are needed for a job of 4000 copies of a book, untrimmed page size 6" × 9", containing 96 pages, printed in 8's sheetwise (16 pages in each form)?

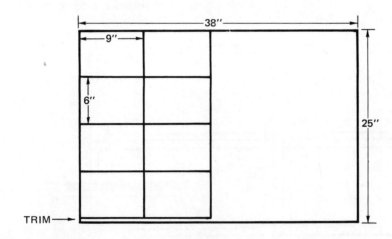

Signature size = (1/8 + 12 + 1/4 + 12 + 1/8) × (1/8 + 9 + 1/4 + 9 + 1/8)
= 24 1/2" × 18 1/2"

Printed both sides yields 16 pages

Signatures per book 96 ÷ 16 = 6

Signatures in the order 6 × 4000 = 24,000

Number of signatures in each sheet of stock

$$\frac{\overset{1}{\cancel{25}} \times \overset{2}{\cancel{38}}}{24\ 1/2 \times 18\ 1/2} = 2 \text{ signatures in each sheet of stock}$$

24,000 ÷ 2 = 12,000 sheets of stock

$$\begin{array}{r} 12,000 \\ +\ 1,200 \\ \hline 13,200 \end{array}$$ 10% of 12,000 for spoilage and overrun/underrun

13,200   sheets of stock 25″ × 38″ needed for the job

PRACTICAL PROBLEMS

In each of the following problems, calculate the stock needed for each order. Cut to get the greatest number of pieces from each piece of stock. Give answers with a 10% allowance for spoilage and overrun/underrun.

1. How many sheets are necessary to cut 6000 pieces of 5″ × 8″ index bristol from 20 1/2″ × <u>24 3/4″</u> − 110? _____

2. How many sheets of index 20 1/2″ × <u>24 3/4″</u> are needed to run 750 5″ × 7″ index cards? _____

3. An order is placed for 7000 billheads measuring 8 1/2″ × 4 3/4″. How many sheets of 17″ × <u>28″</u> bond are required to fill the order? _____

4. How many sheets of 17″ × <u>22″</u> stock are required to run 18,000 billheads measuring 8 1/2″ × 5 1/2″? _____

5. How many sheets of 17″ × <u>22″</u> bond paper are used in order to obtain 10,000 pieces that measure 4″ × 7″? _____

6. Find the amount of stock necessary to print 15,000 32-page catalogs, untrimmed page size 6″ × 9 1/4″, cut from coated stock 25″ × <u>38″</u> − 70. Print in 16's sheetwise. _____

7. How many sheets of 17″ × <u>22″</u> bond paper are required for 6500 notices cut to 3″ × 6 1/4″? _____

8. An order is placed for 5000 billheads measuring 8 1/2″ × 4 3/4″. How many sheets of 17″ × <u>22″</u> bond paper are required to fill this order? _____

9. How much stock is needed for 8000 16-page booklets, trimmed page size 6 3/4″ × 7 1/8″, cut from stock <u>17″</u> × 28″ − 20? Print in 8's sheetwise. _____

10. Find the amount of stock needed for 25,000 32-page booklets, untrimmed page size 6″ × 9″, cut from book paper 25″ × <u>38″</u> − 60. Print in 2's sheetwise. _____

Unit 35 CHARGING FOR CUTTING AND HANDLING STOCK

BASIC PRINCIPLES

- Apply the principles of charging for cutting and handling stock to the printing and graphic communications industry by solving the practical problems in this unit.

An important aspect of estimating costs is the charge for cutting the paper. Paper is cut by the lift. A *lift* is the maximum number of sheets of paper stock that can be placed under the knife of the cutting machine at one time. Each printing shop has its own charges for cutting. This text uses the table below. Additional changes or deletions: for cut apart only, deduct 40%; for back trimming, add 50%.

CUTTING

Table C-1
Bond, Ledger, Book, Newsprint

500 sheets to a lift.
If only 250 sheets can be cut to a lift, add 100%.
If 1,000 sheets can be cut to a lift, deduct 50%.

Sq. In. to Finished Pc.	Number of Finished Size Pieces											Add'l 1 m
	100	500	1m	2m	3m	5m	10m	15m	25m	50m	100m	
20	$1.40	$1.70	$2.10	$2.75	$3.40	$4.70	$7.90	$11.15	$17.55	$33.65	$65.80	$.64
30	1.40	1.75	2.15	2.85	3.55	4.90	8.25	11.65	18.40	35.35	69.20	.68
40	1.40	1.75	2.15	2.95	3.65	5.05	8.60	12.15	19.25	37.05	72.55	.71
50	1.45	1.80	2.20	3.00	3.75	5.25	8.95	12.70	20.10	38.70	75.90	.74
60	1.45	1.80	2.25	3.10	3.85	5.40	9.30	13.20	20.95	40.40	79.30	.78
80	1.45	1.85	2.35	3.25	4.10	5.75	10.00	14.20	22.65	43.80	86.00	.84
100	1.45	1.90	2.40	3.40	4.30	6.10	10.70	15.25	24.35	47.15	92.75	.91
125	1.45	1.95	2.50	3.60	4.60	6.55	11.55	16.55	26.50	51.40	101.20	1.00
173	1.50	2.05	2.75	3.95	5.15	7.45	13.25	19.10	30.75	59.85	118.05	1.16
200	1.50	2.10	2.85	4.15	5.40	7.90	14.15	20.35	32.85	64.05	126.45	1.25
250	1.55	2.20	3.05	4.55	5.95	8.80	15.85	22.95	37.10	72.50	143.30	1.42
350	1.60	2.45	3.45	5.30	7.05	10.55	19.30	28.05	45.60	89.40	177.00	1.75
400	1.60	2.55	3.65	5.70	7.60	11.45	21.05	30.65	49.85	97.85	193.85	1.92
500	1.65	2.75	4.05	6.45	8.70	13.20	24.50	35.75	58.35	114.75	227.55	2.26
700	1.75	3.20	4.90	7.95	10.90	16.75	31.40	46.05	75.30	148.50	294.90	2.93
800	1.80	3.40	5.30	8.75	12.00	18.55	34.85	51.15	83.80	165.40	328.60	3.26
1000	1.90	3.85	6.10	10.25	14.20	22.05	41.75	61.45	100.80	199.20	396.00	394
1600	2.20	5.15	8.55	14.85	20.80	32.70	62.45	92.25	151.75	300.55	598.15	5.96
2000	2.40	6.00	10.20	17.90	25.20	39.80	76.30	112.75	185.70	368.10	732.90	7.30

Table C-2
Cardboard, Cover, Index Bristol, Tagboard

200 sheets to a lift.
If only 100 sheets can be cut to a lift, add 100%.
If 400 sheets can be cut to a lift, deduct 50%.

Sq. In. to Finished Pc.	Number of Finished Size Pieces											Add'l 1 m
	100	500	1m	2m	3m	5m	10m	15m	25m	50m	100m	
15	$1.50	$2.15	$2.85	$4.20	$5.50	$8.05	$14.45	$20.85	$33.60	$65.55	$129.45	$1.27
20	1.50	2.15	2.90	4.30	5.65	8.30	14.90	21.50	34.70	67.70	133.70	1.31
30	1.55	2.20	3.05	4.50	5.90	8.70	15.75	22.75	36.80	71.90	142.10	1.40
40	1.55	2.25	3.15	4.70	6.20	9.15	16.60	24.05	38.90	76.10	150.50	1.48
50	1.55	2.30	3.25	4.90	6.45	9.60	17.45	25.35	41.05	80.35	158.95	1.57
60	1.55	2.40	3.35	5.10	6.75	10.05	18.35	26.60	43.15	84.55	167.35	1.65
80	1.60	2.50	3.55	5.45	7.30	10.95	20.05	29.15	47.40	93.00	184.20	1.82
100	1.60	2.60	3.75	5.85	7.85	11.80	21.80	31.75	51.65	101.45	201.05	1.99
125	1.65	2.75	4.00	6.30	8.50	12.95	23.95	34.95	56.95	112.00	222.10	2.20
150	1.70	2.85	4.25	6.80	9.20	14.05	26.10	38.15	62.30	122.60	243.20	2.41
175	1.70	3.00	4.50	7.25	9.90	15.15	28.25	41.35	67.60	133.15	264.25	2.62
225	1.80	3.25	5.05	8.25	11.25	17.35	32.55	47.80	78.20	154.25	306.35	3.04
300	1.85	3.70	5.80	9.65	13.35	20.70	39.05	57.40	94.10	185.90	369.50	3.67
350	1.95	3.95	6.30	10.60	14.70	22.90	43.35	63.80	104.75	207.05	411.65	4.09
450	2.05	4.50	7.35	12.55	17.45	27.35	52.00	76.65	125.95	249.25	495.85	4.93
600	2.25	5.30	8.85	15.40	21.60	34.00	64.95	95.90	157.80	312.60	622.20	6.19
700	2.40	5.85	9.90	17.30	24.35	38.40	73.55	108.75	179.05	354.85	706.45	7.03
900	2.65	6.95	11.95	21.15	29.85	47.25	90.85	134.80	221.50	439.30	874.90	8.71
1000	2.75	7.45	12.95	23.05	32.60	51.70	99.45	147.20	242.75	481.55	959.15	9.55

The cost of handling stock before and after printing is an expense and an additional charge against the cost of the job. Most printers add 10% to the cost of the material used to cover the cost and expense of trucking, uncrating, unwrapping, storage on shelves, seasoning, jogging, and conveying to the press. Some printers include the cost of cutting in the handling charge.

Cost of Cutting Stock

1. Calculate the area in the finished piece.

2. Look for the appropriate charge on the chart.

   If the number of square inches in the finished piece is not on the chart, go to the next highest figure.

<u>Examples</u>

1. What is the charge for cutting 5000 4″ × 5″ pieces of book trimmed to uniform size?

   Area of finished piece 4″ × 5″ = 20 sq in
   Cutting charge for 5M = $4.70

2. What is the cutting charge for 10,000 6 1/4″ × 8 3/4″ pieces of bond trimmed to uniform size?

   Area of finished piece 6 1/4″ × 8 3/4″ = 54 11/16 sq in
   Cutting charge for 10M = $9.30
   If the number of finished pieces is not on the chart, prorate the cutting charge.

3. What is the cutting charge for 5500 pieces of bond 5″ × 8″ trimmed to uniform size?

   Area of finished piece 5″ × 8″ = 40 sq in
   Cutting charge for 5M = $5.05
   Cutting charge for 10M = $8.60
   Cutting charge per 1000 over 5000 = (8.60 − 5.05) 1/5 = .71
   Cutting charge for 5500 = 5.05 + .36 = $5.41

4. What is the cutting charge for 20,000 pieces of book 9″ × 12″ trimmed to uniform size?

   Area of finished piece 9″ × 12″ = 108 sq in
   Cutting charge for 15M = $16.55
   Cutting charge for 25M = $26.50
   Cutting charge per 1000 over 15M = (26.50 − 16.55) 1/10 = .995
   Cutting charge for 20M = 16.55 + (5 × .995) = $21.53

PRACTICAL PROBLEMS

In each of the following, determine the cutting charge.

1. 10M book 5″ × 6″ trimmed to uniform size _____

2. 15M bond 6″ × 10″ trimmed to uniform size _____

3. 25M bond 3″ × 5″ trimmed to uniform size _____

4. 2M bond 5″ × 7″ trimmed to uniform size _____

5. 3M index 6 1/2″ × 7 5/8″ trimmed to uniform size _____

6. 12M book 8″ × 10″ trimmed to uniform size _____

7. 30M bond 9″ × 11 1/2″ cut apart only _____

8. 45M cover 15 1/2″ × 20 3/4″ trimmed to uniform size _____

9. 35M book 7″ × 5″ cut apart only _____

10. 75M bond 8 1/2″ × 11″ back trimmed _____

Unit 36 FIGURING WEIGHT OF PAPER STOCK

BASIC PRINCIPLES

- Apply the principles of figuring weight of paper stock to the printing and graphic communications industry by solving the practical problems in this unit.

Weight of Stock for an Order

When calculating the weight of stock for an order, the weight is figured on the entire stock which must be used for the order, including waste.

To find the weight of a specified number of sheets of stock, multiply the number of sheets of stock times the weight per sheet. To find the weight per sheet, find the weight per 1000 and divide by 1000.

$$\textbf{Weight of stock = number of sheets of stock} \times \frac{\textbf{weight per 1000}}{\textbf{1000}}$$

<u>Examples</u>

1. Find the weight of 725 sheets of 17″ × 28″ substance 20 bond paper.

    Weight per 1000 = $\dfrac{20}{17 \times 22} \times 17 \times 28 \times 2 = 51$ lb

    Weight of stock = $725 \times \dfrac{51}{1000} = 725 \times .051 = 37$ lb

2. Find the weight of the stock needed for 20,000 16-page booklets, trimmed page size 6″ × 8″, cut from 17″ × 28″ bond paper. Cut in 8's sheetwise.

    There will be 16 page in 1 signature, each 16 1/2″ × 24 1/2″.
    Number of signatures per sheet of stock

    $$\frac{\overset{1}{\cancel{17}} \times \overset{1}{\cancel{28}}}{16\ 1/\cancel{2} \times 2\cancel{4}\ 1/2} = 1$$

    Number of sheets of stock needed 20,000 ÷ 1 + 10% × 20,000 = 22,000 sheets of stock

    Weight per 1000 = $\dfrac{40}{17 \times 22} \times 17 \times 28 \times 2 = 102$ lb

    Weight of stock = $22,000 \times \dfrac{102}{1000} = 22,000 \times .102 = 2244$ lb

Determining the Weight of the Stock Actually Used

When mailing and shipping printed material, it is necessary to calculate the weight of the stock that is actually being shipped.

To calculate the weight of the stock actually shipped, multiply the number of printed sheets times the weight of each sheet.

<u>Examples</u>

1. What is the weight of 2000 pieces of 3″ × 5″ cut from 17″ × <u>22</u>″ substance 20 bond paper?

Weight per 1000 = $\dfrac{20}{17 \times 22}$ × 3 × 5 × 2 = 1.6 lb

Weight of stock used = 2000 × $\dfrac{1.6}{1000}$ = 2000 × .0016 = 3.2 lb

2. What is the weight of 45,000 pieces of 6 1/4″ × 7 1/8″ cut from 38″ × <u>50</u>″ substance 120 book paper?

Weight per 1000 × $\dfrac{120}{25 \times 38}$ × 6 1/4 × 7 1/8 × 2 = 11.25 lb

Weight of stock used = 45,000 × $\dfrac{11.25}{1000}$ = 45,000 × .01125 = 506 1/4 lb

PRACTICAL PROBLEMS

A. In the following problems, calculate the weight of the stock for each order cut to obtain the greatest number of pieces from each stock sheet.

1. What is the weight of 1750 sheets of 34″ × <u>45</u>″ substance 45 book paper? _____

2. Find the weight of 2575 sheets of 17 1/2″ × <u>22 1/2</u>″ substance 40 bond paper. _____

3. What is the weight of 375 sheets of <u>25 1/2</u>″ × 30 1/2″ substance 90 index paper? _____

4. Find the weight of 1875 sheets of 55″ × <u>45</u>″ substance 70 text paper. _____

5. Find the weight of 235 sheets of 23″ × <u>29</u>″ substance 50 book paper. _____

6. Find the weight of the stock needed for 6000 pieces of 5″ × 8″ cut from 25 1/2″ × <u>30 1/2</u>″ substance 90 index paper. _____

7. Find the weight of the stock needed for an order of 25,000 6″ × 9″ pieces cut from 25″ × <u>38</u>″ – 70 book paper? _____

8. Find the weight of the stock needed for an order of 6000 pieces of 4″ × 7″ cut from 17″ × <u>28</u>″ – 44 bond paper. _____

9. What is the weight of the stock needed to make 5000 4-page programs, each page 5″ × 7″, printed in 2's sheetwise on 24″ × <u>34″</u> – 51 bond paper? _____

10. What is the weight of the stock needed for an order of 25,000 32-page booklets, each untrimmed page 8″ × 10″, printed in 8's sheetwise on 35″ × <u>45″</u> – 32 bond paper? _____

B. Find the weight of each of the following pieces.

1. 50 pieces 3″ × 5″ cut from 17″ × <u>28″</u> substance 20 bond paper _____

2. 75 pieces 4″ × 6″ cut from 25″ × <u>38″</u> substance 60 bond paper _____

3. 650 pieces 3 1/2″ × 5 3/4″ cut from 35″ × <u>45″</u> substance 80 book paper _____

4. 40,000 pieces 7″ × 9″ cut from 35″ × <u>46″</u> substance 130 cover paper _____

5. 2575 pieces 6″ × 8 5/8″ cut from 24″ × <u>36″</u> substance 90 index paper _____

6. 4630 pieces 3″ × 5″ cut from 24″ × <u>34″</u> substance 49 bond paper _____

7. 685 pieces 2 1/2″ × 4 3/4″ cut from 23″ × <u>35″</u> substance 70 bond paper _____

8. 760 pieces 9″ × 12″ cut from 20″ × <u>26″</u> substance 50 cover paper _____

9. 975 pieces 8″ × 6″ cut from 35″ × <u>45″</u> substance 30 book paper _____

10. 43,500 pieces 7″ × 5″ cut from 28″ × <u>34″</u> substance 28 bond paper _____

Unit 37 FIGURING COST OF PAPER STOCK

BASIC PRINCIPLES

- Apply the principles of figuring the cost of paper stock to the printing and graphic communications industry by solving the practical problems in this unit.

Figuring Cost Using CWT Price

Most paper used in printing is priced per hundredweight (cwt). To figure the cost of an order, use the following procedure.

1. Find the number of stock sheets needed for the order (plus 10% for spoilage and overrun/underrun).

2. Find the weight per sheet.

3. Multiply the number of sheets of stock needed for the order by the price per cwt and divide by 100.

$$\textbf{Price = sheets of stock} \times \frac{\textbf{weight per M}}{\textbf{1000}} \times \frac{\textbf{price per cwt}}{\textbf{100}}$$

Examples

1. What is the cost of 5000 sheets, size 5 1/2″ × 8 1/2″, to be cut from 17″ × 22″ − 20 at $55.65 cwt? Cut to obtain the greatest number of pieces per sheet of stock.

   Pieces per sheet of stock

   $$\frac{\overset{3}{1\cancel{7}} \times \overset{2}{2\cancel{2}}}{5\ 1/2 \times 8\ 1/2} = 6 \text{ pieces}$$

   $$\frac{\overset{2}{\cancel{17}} \times \overset{4}{\cancel{22}}}{\cancel{5\ 1/2} \times \cancel{8\ 1/2}} = 8 \text{ pieces}$$

   Number of sheets of stock needed 5000 ÷ 8 + 10% × 625 = 688 sheets

   Weight for order = 688 × $\frac{40}{1000}$ = 27.5 lb

   Price = 27.5 × $\frac{55.65}{100}$ = $15.30

2. What is the cost of 40,000 pieces, size 3 1/2″ × 5 1/2″, cut from 35″ × 46″ substance 100 book paper priced at $50.80 cwt?

Pieces per sheet of stock

$$\frac{\overset{10}{3\cancel{5}} \times \overset{8}{4\cancel{6}}}{3\ 1/2 \times 5\ 1/2} = 80 \text{ pieces}$$

$$\frac{\overset{6}{35} \times \overset{13}{46}}{3\ 1/2 \times 5\ 1/2} = 78 \text{ pieces}$$

Number of sheets of stock needed 40,000 ÷ 80 + 10% of 500 = 550 sheets

Weight per 1000 sheets of stock $= \dfrac{100}{25 \times 38} \times 35 \times 46 \times 2 = 339$ lb

Weight for order $= 550 \times \dfrac{339}{1000} = 186.5$ lb

Price $= 186.5 \times \dfrac{50.80}{100} = \$94.74$

Figuring Cost Using 1000-Sheet Price

Stock is also priced per 1000 sheets. To calculate the cost of an order, use the following procedure.

1. Find the number of sheets of stock needed.

2. Divide by 1000.

3. Multiply by the price per 1000 sheets.

$$\textbf{Price} = \frac{\textbf{sheets of stock}}{\textbf{1000}} \times \textbf{price per 1000}$$

Examples

1. Find the price of 50,000 covers size 9″ × 12″, cut from 32″ × 44″ substance 80 book paper priced at $47.03 per 1000 sheets.

Number of pieces from a sheet of stock

$$\frac{\overset{3}{3\cancel{2}} \times \overset{3}{4\cancel{4}}}{\cancel{9} \times 1\cancel{2}} = 9 \text{ pieces}$$

$$\frac{\overset{2}{32} \times \overset{4}{44}}{9 \times 12} = 8 \text{ pieces}$$

Number of sheets of stock needed 50,000 ÷ 9 + 10% of 5556 = 6112 sheets

Price $= \dfrac{6112}{1000} \times 47.03 = \$287.45$

2. A manufacturer orders 2500, 12-page booklets. Each page measures 8″ × 9 1/2″ and is to be run in three 4-page forms on 38″ × 50″ – 60 book paper. If the stock costs $91.68 per 1000 sheets, what is the cost of the stock for this order?

Number of pieces per sheet of stock

$$\frac{\overset{2}{38} \times \overset{5}{50}}{16 \; 1/2 \times 10} = 10 \text{ pieces}$$

Number of 4-page forms needed 2500 × 3 = 7500
Number of sheets of stock needed 7500 ÷ 10 + 10% of 750 = 825 sheets

$$\text{Price} = \frac{825}{1000} \times 91.68 = \$75.64$$

PRACTICAL PROBLEMS

A. Find the price of the stock needed for each of the following orders. Cut to obtain the greatest number of pieces with grain all the same direction.

1. 4500 sheets of 19″ × 24″ substance 20 bond priced at $62.60 cwt   _____

2. 50,000 sheets of 32″ × 44″ substance 60 book priced at $93.65 cwt   _____

3. 10,000 slips of paper 3″ × 5″ cut from 17″ × 22″ – 16 bond priced at $67.65 cwt   _____

4. 7000 cards 3 1/2″ × 5 1/4″ cut from 20 1/2″ × 24 3/4″ – 90 index priced at $59.20 cwt   _____

5. 1500, 12-page bulletins, printed in three 4-page forms, folded 8″ × 10″, cut from 35″ × 45″ substance 80 book priced at $75.55 cwt   _____

6. 2500, 4-page booklets printed in 2's sheetwise, page size 8″ × 12″, cut from 38″ × 50″ substance 80 book priced at $72.95 cwt   _____

7. 20M sets, numbered in triplicate, 8 1/2″ × 11″, cut from white 17″ × 22″ – 20 bond priced at $67.65, and from canary and green priced at $70.25 cwt   _____

8. 6000 sheets 5 1/2″ × 8 1/2″ cut from 24″ × 34″ substance 20 bond priced at $62.60 cwt   _____

9. 6000 billheads 5 1/2″ × 8 1/2″ cut from 22″ × 34″ substance 20 bond priced at $52.15 cwt   _____

10. 4500, 12-page pamphlets printed in three 4-page forms, page size 6″ × 8″, cut from 25″ × <u>38</u>″ – 60 book priced at $70.40 cwt _____

B. Find the cost of the stock needed for each of the following orders.

1. 350 pieces 3″ × 5″ cut from 17″ × <u>22</u>″ – 20 bond priced at $25.44 per 1000 sheets _____

2. 775 pieces 4″ × 6″ cut from 25″ × <u>38</u>″ – 60 book priced at $91.68 per 1000 sheets _____

3. 10,000 copies of a 16-page booklet printed in 8's sheetwise, untrimmed folded size 6″ × 9″, cut from 25″ × <u>38</u>″ – 80 priced at $116.72 per 1000 sheets _____

4. 2500, 4-page booklets, printed in 2's sheetwise, page size 8″ × 12″, cut from 25″ × <u>38</u>″ – 16 bond, priced at $55.15 per 1000 sheets _____

5. 3000 copies of a 4-page folder cut in 2's sheetwise, size 9″ × 11 1/2″, cut from 23″ × <u>35</u>″ substance 120 bristol priced at $221.10 per 1000 sheets _____

6. 4200 inserts for a book 6″ × 9″, cut from 25″ × <u>38</u>″ substance 80, priced at $91.92 per 1000 sheets _____

7. 50,000 covers 9″ × 12″, cut from <u>35</u>″ × 46″ substance 80 cover, priced at $404.98 per 1000 sheets _____

8. 25,000 record slips 4″ × 6″, printed on 17″ × <u>22</u>″ – 24 bond priced at $34.15 per 1000 sheets _____

9. 18,000 office forms 4 1/2″ × 6″, printed on 19″ × <u>24</u>″ #4 sulfite bond, priced at $25.99 per 1000 sheets _____

10. 125,000 handbills 3 1/2″ × 6 1/4″, printed on 25″ × <u>38</u>″ substance 70 coated back, priced at $107.52 per 1000 sheets _____

ACHIEVEMENT REVIEW A

The number found in the parentheses after each problem indicates the unit in which similar problems were discussed.

1. A printing firm prints 18,250 tags on Monday, 17,125 tags on Tuesday, 16,350 tags on Wednesday, 18,825 tags on Thursday, and 17,450 tags on Friday. The following week, 5000 more tags than during the preceding week are printed. How many tags are printed in the 2 weeks? (1)

2. If an instant print shop has 38,000 sheets of bond paper on hand and uses 13,500 sheets, how much stock is left? (2)

3. An estimate is prepared for a customer's catalog. It is determined that 45 large plates are needed to complete a job. The total cost for the metal plates is $360. What is the cost for each plate? (4)

4. A certain job ticket has the following times recorded: artwork, 3 1/2 hours; composition, 1 1/2 hours; camera, 3/4 hour; stripping, 1/2 hour; prepress color proofing, 1 3/4 hours. What is the total time recorded on this job ticket? (6)

5. When the regular monthly inventory is conducted, the person counting finds 29 3/5 reams. The inventory record indicates 32 1/2 reams. How much in error is the inventory record? (7)

6. A ream of paper weighs 16 3/4 pounds. How many pounds of paper are contained on a skid containing 40 3/4 reams? (8)

7. A camera operator, using an automatic camera attached to a processor, puts out 174 line negatives during 7 3/10 hours. How many shots are made during the average hour? (9)

8. A keyliner puts the following measurements on the art board for the placement of type and artwork. Left margin, .75 inch; text, 4.125 inches; screened print, 3.5 inches; right margin, .75 inch. What is the total width of this job? (10)

9. A 42-pica line of type is set. The type style is Goudy Extrabold 12-point type. Eighty-six typewritten letters fit into this line. Calculate to the nearest thousandths the characters per pica? (13)

10. A bill that amounts to $179.65 for letterheads and envelopes is submitted to a customer. In this amount, the printer includes $22 profit. What is the percent of profit for this transaction? (15)

11. In order to purchase needed equipment, a printer borrows $12,350 which is repaid at the end of 7 months. If the rate of interest is 15% per annum, find the amount of interest paid by the printer. (16)

12. What is the net amount of a printing bill of $603.50 if the discounts are 30% and 10%? (17)

13. A print shop owner purchases 700, 10″ × 15″ pb litho plates. The price is $1.32 per plate. The next day, the price of these plates increases 8 3/4%. How much is saved by purchasing the plates at the lower price? (17)

14. Copy that is now set in a space 24 × 36 picas is to be reset to fit a type page set 36 picas wide. What should the other dimension be? (18)

15. Find the area of a rectangle 3 1/2″ × 5 3/4″. (21)

16. Find the area of a rectangle 23.7 cm by 35.7 cm. (22)

17. A job is printed on stock cut 8 1/2 inches wide by 11 inches deep. Find the dimensions of the stock in picas. (25)

18. What part of an inch is 54 points? (25)

19. How many columns 2 1/2 picas wide can fit into 27 1/2 picas? (25)

20. If a line of 6-point type measures 28 picas, how many ems does the line contain? (26)

21. How many lines of 9-point type are in a page 7 inches deep? (26)

22. Find the number of ems in a page 50 picas long, 48 picas wide, set in 8-point type set solid. (26)

23. Find the number of ems contained in a form 28 picas wide by 216 picas deep, set 8 on 12. (27)

24. Find the number of lines needed for a manuscript containing 6354 characters, set 10-point Antique Olive (2.1405 characters per pica) 36 picas wide. (28)

25. Find the number of words of copy that will fit in a space 24 × 36 picas, set Goudy Bold 10/12 (2.3871 characters per pica). (28)

26. Find the cost of a book containing 350 pages if it is set 10/12 with a page size of 24 × 36 picas. Use the em method ($1.15 per 100 ems), and set in excellent quality (75%). (28)

27. An order calls for 85,000 sheets of bond 20 pounds per ream. How many reams are there in the order? How many 1500-pound skids are in the order? (30)

28. What is the basic size of bond paper? (31)

29. What is the weight of 1000 sheets of paper 24″ × 36″ if the basic size is 25″ × 38″ and the basic weight is 60 pounds? (32)

30. How many pieces 5″ × 7″ can be cut from a sheet of stock measuring 38″ × 50″? (Observe the grain direction.) (33)

31. How many pieces of stock 4″ × 6″ can be cut from a sheet of stock measuring 28″ × 35″? (Cut either with the grain or across the grain.) (33)

32. Which of the following sheets of stock will cut pieces 5″ × 6″ most economically: 17″ × 22″, 19″ × 24″, or 28″ × 34″? (Observe the grain direction.) (34)

33. How many sheets are needed to cut 7000 pieces of 5″ × 8″ bond from 17″ × 28″ − 20? (Calculate for spoilage. Cut to get the greatest number of pieces.) (35)

34. Find the amount of stock needed for 30,000, 16-page booklets, untrimmed page size 6″ × 9″ cut from 25″ × 38″ − 60 book paper. Print in 8's sheetwise. (Calculate for spoilage.) (35)

35. Find the cutting charge for 30M 5″ × 9″ pieces of bond trimmed to uniform size. (Use the chart in Unit 35.) (35)

36. Find the weight of the stock needed for an order of 8000, 4-page booklets, each page 5″ × 7″ printed in 2's sheetwise on 24″ × 34″ – 49 bond. (37)

37. Find the weight of 50,000 pieces of 3 1/2″ × 5 3/4″ cut from 35″ × 45″ – 100 book. (37)

38. Find the cost of 2000, 4-page booklets printed in 2's sheetwise page size 8″ × 12″, cut from 38″ × 50″ – 80 book priced at $72.95 cwt. (38)

39. Calculate the cost of 8000 sheets of 5 1/2″ × 8 1/2″ cut from 25″ × 38″ – 70 book, priced at $107.52 per 1000 sheets. (38)

ACHIEVEMENT REVIEW B

1. Publication A contains 11,943 ems of type, publication B contains 12,497 ems of type, publication C has 13,237 ems of type, publication D has 14,306 ems of type, and publication E has 22,427 ems of type. What is the total ems of type set in these publications? (1)

2. A certain job consists of 78,500 ems of type. The phototypesetter sets 35,640 ems the first day. How many ems need to be set the second day to complete the job? (2)

3. A booklet contains 2478 lines of 8-point type. Find the number of pages if each page has 42 lines. (4)

4. During a certain week, the camera department works on several jobs. Their productive time is recorded as follows: Monday, 7 8/10 hours; Tuesday, 8 3/10 hours; Wednesday, 6 4/10 hours; Thursday, 6 9/10 hours; Friday, 5 4/10 hours. What is the total productive time during the week? (6)

5. A printer has 9 3/4 reams of book paper on hand. If the printer uses 1 1/5 of a ream on a short run, how many reams remain? (7)

6. A press run is consuming an average of 4 9/16 pounds of black ink per hour. For a certain job, the press is run for 8 3/10 hours. How many pounds of black ink are used? (8)

7. A manuscript contains 12,578 words. Each page of type averages 212 1/2 words. How many pages will the finished job contain? (9)

8. How many hours are charged to a job that takes 4.3 hours in typesetting, 3.7 hours in keylining, 1.8 hours in camera, 1.7 hours in stripping, .75 hour in platemaking? (10)

9. A sales representative sells $10,922.09 worth of printing during a 4.5-day week. What is the sales representative's average sales per day? (13)

10. The stock on a job costs $15.10 and the cost of printing the job is $7.75. If the printer figures 20% profit on the stock and 30% profit on the cost of printing, what is the amount of the bill for the job? (15)

11. The cost of a new trimmer is $4595.00. The printer borrows $5000 at 14 3/4% per annum and repays the loan after 7 months. The trimmer is sold for $5050.00. How much is gained or lost on the transaction? (16)

12. Upon purchasing a quantity of ink priced at $289, a printer is allowed a direct discount of 32 1/2%, and if the bill is paid within 30 days, a cash discount of 2% is allowed. What is the net bill? (17)

13. Because of certain mistakes made by a printer on an order of forms costing $1347.65, the customer agrees to buy them if the forms are discounted 27%. What is the sale price? (18)

14. A photo measuring 5" × 7" is made into a cut for the editorial page of a newspaper. The editorial column is 18 picas wide. How deep is the cut? (19)

15. Find the area of a rectangle 4 3/4" × 6 7/8". (21)

16. Find the area of a rectangle 455 mm × 645 mm. (22)

17. A form measures 4 7/8 inches wide by 5 3/8 inches deep. Give the size of the form in picas. (25)

18. What part of an inch is 6 points? (25)

19. What is the width of each column if 8 columns are fit into 46 picas? (25)

20. If a line of 8-point type measure 5 1/2 inches, how many ems does the line contain? (26)

21. How many lines of 10-point type are contained in a page 75 picas deep? (26)

22. Find the number of ems in a page 6 inches long, 8 inches wide, set in 6-point type set solid. (26)

23. How many ems of 8-point type, 2 points extra leading, are set in a leaflet having 4 pages, if each page is printed with forms 6 inches wide and 7 1/2 inches deep? (27)

24. Find the number of lines needed for a manuscript containing 15,243 characters, set 12-point English Times (2.1405 characters per pica), set 45 picas wide. (28)

25. Find the number of words of copy that fit into a space 36 × 45 picas set Antique Olive 8/10 (2.7120 characters per pica). (28)

26. Find the cost of a book containing 280 pages if it is set 8/10 with a page size of 35 × 45 picas. Use the em method ($1.45 per 100 ems) and set in excellent quality (75%). (29)

27. An order calls for 80,000 sheets of book 60 pounds per ream. How many reams are contained in the order? How many 1500-pound skids are contained in the order? (30)

28. What is the basic size of book paper? (31)

29. What is the weight of 1000 sheets of paper 25″ × 38″ if the basic size is 17″ × 22″ and the basic weight is 49 pounds? (32)

30. How many pieces 5″ × 3″ can be cut from a sheet of stock measuring 22″ × 34″? (Observe the grain direction.) (33)

31. How many pieces of stock 3″ × 5″ can be cut from a sheet of stock measuring 17″ × 22″? (Cut either with the grain or across the grain.) (33)

32. Which of the following sheets of stock will cut pieces 3″ × 5″ most economically: 25″ × 38″, 20″ × 26″, or 38″ × 50″? (Observe the grain direction) (34)

33. How many sheets of 25″ × 38″ stock are needed to cut 10,000, 6″ × 9 1/4″ pieces? (Calculate for spoilage. Cut to get the greatest number of pieces.) (35)

34. How much stock is needed for 25,000, 8-page booklets, untrimmed size 6 3/4″ × 7″, cut from bond 17″ × 28″? Print in 4's sheetwise. (Calculate for spoilage.) (35)

35. Find the cutting charge for 45M 3 1/2″ × 5 3/4″ pieces of book trimmed to uniform size. (Use the chart in Unit 35.) (35)

36. Find the weight of the stock needed for an order of 10,000, 16-page booklets, each page 8″ × 10″, printed in 8's sheetwise on 35″ × <u>45</u>″ − 20 bond paper. (37)

37. Find the weight of 20,000 pieces of 4″ × 6″ cut from 25″ × <u>38</u>″ − 60 bond. (37)

38. Find the cost of 6000, 12-page booklets printed in three 4-page forms, page size 5″ × 8″, cut from 32″ × 44″ − 60 book, priced at $93.65 cwt. (38)

39. Calculate the cost of 10,000 sheets of 6″ × 9″ cut from 25″ × 38″ − 80 book, priced at $91.92 per 1000 sheets. (38)

APPENDIX

DENOMINATE NUMBERS

Denominate numbers are numbers that include units of measurement. The units of measurement are arranged from the largest units at the left to the smallest unit at the right.

For example: 6 yd 2 ft 4 in

All basic operations of arithmetic can be performed on denominate numbers.

I. EQUIVALENT MEASURES

Measurements that are equal can be expressed in different terms. For example, 12 in = 1 ft. If these equivalents are divided, the answer is 1.

$$\frac{1 \text{ ft}}{12 \text{ in}} = 1 \qquad \frac{12 \text{ in}}{1 \text{ ft}} = 1$$

To express one measurement as another equal measurement, multiply by the equivalent in the form of 1.

To express 6 inches in equivalent foot measurement, multiply 6 inches by one in the form of

$\frac{1 \text{ ft}}{12 \text{ in}}$. In the numerator and denominator, divide by a common factor.

$$6 \text{ in } = \frac{\overset{1}{\cancel{6 \text{ in}}}}{1} \times \frac{1}{\underset{2}{\cancel{12 \text{ in}}}} = \frac{1}{2} \text{ ft or } 0.5 \text{ ft}$$

To express 4 feet in equivalent inch measurement, multiply 4 feet by one in the form of

$\frac{12 \text{ in}}{1 \text{ ft}}$.

$$4 \text{ ft } = \overset{4}{\cancel{4 \text{ ft}}} \times \frac{12 \text{ in}}{\underset{1}{\cancel{1 \text{ ft}}}} = \frac{48 \text{ in}}{1} = 48 \text{ in}$$

Per means division, as with a fraction bar. For example, 50 miles per hour can be written

$\frac{50 \text{ miles}}{1 \text{ hour}}$.

II. BASIC OPERATIONS

A. ADDITION

SAMPLE: 2 yd 1 ft 5 in + 1 ft 8 in + 5 yd 2 ft

1. Write the denominate numbers in a column with like units in the same column.

	2 yd	1 ft	5 in
		1 ft	8 in
+	5 yd	2 ft	

2. Add the denominate numbers in each column.

	7 yd	4 ft	13 in

3. Express the answer using the largest possible units.

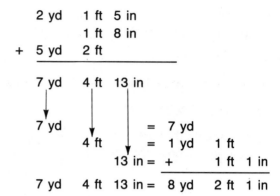

	7 yd	4 ft	13 in =	8 yd	2 ft	1 in

B. SUBTRACTION

SAMPLE: 4 yd 3 ft 5 in − 2 yd 1 ft 7 in

1. Write the denominate numbers in columns with like units in the same column.

	4 yd	3 ft	5 in
−	2 yd	1 ft	7 in

2. Starting at the right, examine each column to compare the numbrs. If the bottom number is larger, exchange one unit from the column at the left for its equivalent. Combine like units.

7 in is larger than 5 in

3 ft = 2 ft 12 in

12 in + 5 in = 17 in

3. Subtract the denominate numbers.

	4 yd	2 ft	17 in
−	2 yd	1 ft	7 in
	2 yd	1 ft	10 in

4. Express the answer using the largest possible units.

2 yd	1 ft	10 in

C. MULTIPLICATION

—*By a constant*

SAMPLE: 1 hr 24 min × 3

1. Multiply the denominate number by the constant.

1 hr	24 min
	× 3
3 hr	72 min

2. Express the answer using the largest possible units.

3 hr		=	3 hr	
	72 min	=	1 hr	12 min
3 hr	72 min	=	4 hr	12 min

—By a denominate number expressing linear measurement

SAMPLE: 9 ft 6 in × 10 ft

1. Express all denominate numbers in the same unit.

$$9 \text{ ft } 6 \text{ in} = 9\frac{1}{2} \text{ ft}$$

2. Multiply the denominate numbers. (This includes the units of measure, such as ft × ft = sq ft.)

$$9\frac{1}{2} \text{ ft} \times 10 \text{ ft} =$$

$$\frac{19}{2} \text{ ft} \times 10 \text{ ft} =$$

$$95 \text{ sq ft}$$

—By a denominate number expressing square measurement

SAMPLE: 3 ft 6 sq ft

1. Multiply the denominate numbers. (This includes the units of measure, such as ft × ft = sq ft and sq ft × ft = cu ft.)

$$3 \text{ ft} \times 6 \text{ sq ft} = 18 \text{ cu ft}$$

—By a denominate number expressing rate

SAMPLE: 50 miles per hour × 3 hours

1. Express the rate as a fraction using the fraction bar for *per*.

$$\frac{50 \text{ miles}}{1 \text{ hour}} \times \frac{3 \text{ hours}}{1} =$$

2. Divide the numerator and denominator by any common factors, including units of measure.

$$\frac{50 \text{ miles}}{\underset{1}{\cancel{1 \text{ hour}}}} \times \frac{\overset{3}{\cancel{3 \text{ hours}}}}{1} =$$

3. Multiply numerators. Multiply denominators

$$\frac{150 \text{ miles}}{1} =$$

4. Express the answer in the remaining unit.

$$150 \text{ miles}$$

D. **DIVISION**

   —By a constant

   SAMPLE: 8 gal 3 qt ÷ 5

1. Express all denominate numbers in the same unit.

$$8 \text{ gal } 3 \text{ qt} = 35 \text{ qt}$$

2. Divide the denominate number by the constant.

$$35 \text{ qt} \div 5 = 7 \text{ qt}$$

3. Express the answer using the largest possible units.

$$7 \text{ qt} = 1 \text{ gal } 3 \text{ qt}$$

—By a denominate number expressing linear measurement

SAMPLE: 11 ft 4 in ÷ 8 in

1. Express all denominate numbers in the same unit.

   11 ft 4 in = 136 in

2. Divide the denominate numbers by a common factor. (This includes the units of measure, such as inches ÷ inches = 1.)

   136 in ÷ 8 in =

   $$\frac{\cancel{136\text{ in}}^{\;17}}{\cancel{8\text{ in}}_{\;1}} = \frac{17}{1} = 17$$

—By a linear measure with a square measurement as the dividend

SAMPLE: 20 sq ft ÷ 4 ft

1. Divide the denominate numbers. (This includes the units of measure, such as sq ft ÷ ft = ft.)

   20 sq ft ÷ 4 ft

   $$\frac{\cancel{20\text{ sq ft}}^{\;5\text{ ft}}}{\cancel{4\text{ ft}}} = \frac{5\text{ ft}}{1}$$

2. Express the answer in the remaining unit.

   5 ft

—By denominate numbers used to find rate

SAMPLE: 200 mi ÷ 10 gal

1. Divide the denominate numbers.

   $$\frac{\cancel{200\text{ mi}}^{\;20\text{ mi}}}{\cancel{10\text{ gal}}_{\;1\text{ gal}}} = \frac{20\text{ mi}}{1\text{ gal}}$$

2. Express the units with the fraction bar meaning *per*.

   $$\frac{20\text{ mi}}{1\text{ gal}} = 20\text{ miles per gallon}$$

Note: Alternate methods of performing the basic operations will produce the same result. The choice of method is determined by the individual.

GLOSSARY

Alpha length — A method for determining characters per pica. The lower case alphabet measured in points.

Backbone — The binding edge of a signature.

Backing up — Printing the other side of a printed sheet.

Basic size — A standard size that various kinds of paper are cut in determining basic weight.

Basic weight — The weight of 500 sheets of a given paper stock cut to its standard or basic size.

Bleed — That portion of the image that is extended into the trim of the paper. It is later cut off to give a neat appearance to the image at the edge of the sheet.

Body type — Composition used in the main text portion of a job. Smaller point sizes are used.

Bundle — A way of packaging a number of sheets of stock such as chipboard and secured by a string or cord.

Characters per pica — The number of typeset characters that will fit within each pica in a line of type. The number varies according to the size and style of type chosen.

Caps — Capital letters in the alphabet.

Carton — A way of packaging paper. The carton may contain a number of packages or loose sheets. The quantity depends on the size and weight of the stock. The average carton weighs approximately 125 lbs.

Centimetre (cm) — Metric measurement. One hundredth part of a metre.

Copy — Manuscript or text furnished to the printer. May also pertain to photographs and artwork.

Copyfitting — A method whereby a manuscript is fit within given specifications. Also determining the amount of copy needed to fill a given space.

Copy preparation (Prep.) — Preparing copy, whether text, photographs and/or artwork for paste-up onto the finished mechanical. The actual work of preparing a mechanical.

Decametre (dkm) — Metric measurement. Equal to ten metres in length.

Decimetre (dm) — Metric measurement. One tenth of a metre.

Dummy — A set of blank pages made up in advance to indicate page imposition, general style and plan. Especially useful in printing books and magazines.

Elite type — Twelve typewriter characters per inch.

Em — Considered the square of the type size with which you may be working. Example: 12-point type has an em size of 12 points.

En — One half of an em.

Face — In letterpress the part of the type that prints. Interchangeable with the word 'font'.

Flat — The assembly of negatives and positives on goldenrod paper or vinyl for exposure to a litho (offset) plate.

Flush left or right — Type that is set to align either on the left or right edge and ragged on the opposite side. May also be referred to as ragged right or left.

Folio — Page number.

Font — A series of characters and figures that make up a complete style and size of type.

Galley — In letterpress, a metal tray that is used to hold type and cuts. A proof from metal type. In phototypesetting, a length of photopaper containing composition for a given job.

Gang — To combine several smaller printing jobs on a larger sheet of paper all having the same color(s) of ink.

Grain — The direction of fibers in a sheet of paper.

Gram (g) — Metric measurement. A basic unit of weight equal to about 1/28 of an ounce.

Gripper — A margin on the lead edge of the press sheet where no printing can occur. A place on the sheet for the mechanical gripper fingers to pull the paper through the press.

Halftone — Tones are represented by evenly spaced dots of various sizes that represent detail and tone values of the original photograph or artwork.

Imposition — The arrangement of pages in their proper sequence on a larger sheet of paper.

Impression — Printing of each color on an individual sheet of paper. Press speed is rated at impressions per hour. In the case of a two-color press each sheet contains two impressions.

Italic — A font of type or face where the letters have a slant.

Justified — Setting of copy by adjusting the space between words so that the type is aligned on both edges or margins.

Keyline — Lines drawn on a mechanical or paste-up to indicate the position of artwork. In recent years has come to mean the same as paste-up or mechanical.

Kilogram (kg) — Metric measurement. One thousand grams.

Leading — (Pronounced 'ledding') The separation between lines of type stated in points and half points.

Litre (L) — Metric measurement. The standard unit of liquid measurement. It is a little larger than the quart.

Lower case — Small letters in the alphabet.

Manuscript — The original written matter from which type is prepared.

Margin — White space between columns and around the edges of type, pictures and artwork.

Mechanical — The finished type and artwork ready for camera.

Metre (m) — Metric measurement. Standard measurement that is a little longer than one yard.

Micrometer — An instrument used to measure accurately the thickness of stock to the nearest thousandth of an inch.

Millilitre (mL) — Metric measurement. One thousandth part of a litre.

Millimetre (mm) — Metric measurement. One thousandth part of a metre.

Package — A way of packaging paper. Paper stock wrapped in paper and usually placed in a master carton. Package sizes range from 100 to 500 sheets.

Pica — Printing measurement. Approximately 1/6 of an inch. Used to measure length of lines and depth of areas.

Pica type — Ten typewriter characters to the inch.

Point — Printing measurement. Measures 0.01384 or approximately 1/72 of an inch. Exactly 12 to the pica.

Quad — Applies to the position of lines of type as they are set, such as quad center, quad left or right. In letterpress, the spacing material to fill out any line.

Ream — Five hundred sheets of paper.

Scale (Proportion Scale) — Usually a circular device with scales for reproduction and original sizes. The resultant answer is given in percentage. An instrument to calculate a new size for artwork and halftones.

Self cover — The cover of a booklet that is printed on the same stock as the inside. The cover will be stripped as a part of the first signature of the booklet.

Sheet-wise — A method of press production. Each side of the press sheet is printed using a different plate. The same edge of the sheet is used for the gripper and guide.

Shingle (Creep) — The effect when the center or inner pages protrude when signatures are assembled as in saddle binding.

Signature — A group of pages printed on one or two sides of a large sheet that is to be folded to become combined with other signatures to become a book.

Skid — A way of packaging paper. Bulk paper secured to a wooden platform. The total weight of paper and skid will weigh between 1500 to 3000 pounds.

Stock — Printing paper.

Straight matter — Text set in paragraph form. No special treatment such as tabulation is performed.

Stripper — A person who positions negatives and positives on flats for the purpose of making printing plates.

Substance — Basic weight of paper.

Tabular matter — Type set in columns. The most common is figures, as in price lists.

Trim — The margin of paper cut away during the finishing operation. Usually 1/8 inch.

Tumble — A method of press production. Forms for both sides of the sheet appear on one side of the printing plate. The entire sheet is printed for half the run and then tumbled over, using the tail of the sheet as the new gripper for the second side.

Work and turn — A method of press production. Forms for both sides of the sheet appear on one side of the printing plate. The entire sheet is printed for half the run and then turned over from left to right and the run completed using the same printing plate as used on the first side. The same gripper edge is used for both sides of the sheet.

ANSWERS TO ODD-NUMBERED PROBLEMS

SECTION 1 WHOLE NUMBERS
Unit 1 Addition of Whole Numbers

1. 65 hr
3. 2422 reams
5. 12,186 sheets

7. 176,144 tags
9. 73,616 ems
11. 794,142 copies

13. 58,104 letterheads
15. 49,750 books

Unit 2 Subtraction of Whole Numbers

1. $1350
3. 14,500 sheets
5. 6378 ems

7. 19,300 signatures
9. $218
11. 32 jobs

13. 2478 ems
15. 24 hr

Unit 3 Multiplication of Whole Numbers

1. $84
3. 224,000 production
5. 10,920 lines

7. $8650
9. 30,000 letterheads
11. 272,160 ems

13. 381,480 cards
15. $93

Unit 4 Division of Whole Numbers

1. 1875 sheets
3. 917 reams
5. $598

7. 4275 circulars/hr
9. $11
11. 9 in

13. 4 oz
15. 41 reams

Unit 5 Roman Numerals

A. 1. XIX
    3. XXV

B. 1. 20
    5. 1350

C. 1. $\overline{VI}$

D. 1. 7

5. XCVI
7. DXLIX

3. 305
7. 504

3. $\overline{LXXV}DXLII$

3. 16

9. MMCDXCIV

9. 999

5. 130,000

SECTION 2 COMMON FRACTIONS
Unit 6 Addition of Fractions

1. 6 1/2 hr
3. 41 1/16 reams
5. 23 in

7. 25 1/2 in
9. 18 3/4 hr
11. 12 in

13. 5 1/8 hr
15. 6 5/8 in

Unit 7 Subtraction of Fractions

1. 2 1/2 hr
3. 8 5/12 reams
5. 3/4 ream

7. 3 7/8 in
9. 9 5/8 in
11. 2 7/10 hr

13. 3 5/16 lb
15. 1 1/6 in

Unit 8 Multiplication of Fractions

1. 26 1/4 hr
3. 58 1/3 picas
5. 38 in

7. 12 15/16 in
9. 1962 1/2 lb
11. 23 1/32 lb

13. 90 hr
15. 830 1/4 lb

Answers to Odd-Numbered Questions

Unit 9 Division of Fractions

1. 1800 char/hr
3. 9250 impressions/hr
5. 27,500 in/hr

7. 20 shots/hr
9. 4 sheets
11. 7 lengths with 1/2″ scrap remaining

13. 4 cuts
15. 3 3/4 picas

SECTION 3 DECIMAL FRACTIONS
Unit 10 Addition of Decimals

1. 10.22 hr
3. 1061.705 lb
5. 7.125 in

7. $38,922.69
9. .1915 in
11. 7.50 hr

13. $2377.12
15. 27.30 in

Unit 11 Subtraction of Decimals

1. $2083.43
3. $2830.46
5. $46.66

7. 1.1 lb
9. $3224.86
11. $96.99

13. 70.33 lb
15. 1.625 in

Unit 12 Multiplication of Decimals

1. $365.63
3. $3118.57
5. $50.99

7. 10.02 in
9. 2868.75 words
11. 21.225 lb

13. $99
15. $37.05

Unit 13 Division of Decimals

1. $1444.48
3. 8800 impressions
5. 27.5 picas

7. $2.46
9. $35.70
11. $30.90

13. 1.75 in
15. 1300 books

SECTION 4 PERCENT
Unit 14 Percent Equivalents

A. 1. .15
   3. 1.45

5. .085
7. 9.25

9. .0481

B. 1. 3/10
   3. 3/400

5. 1/16
7. 1/3

9. 1/8

C. 1. 20%
   3. 31.5%

5. 62.5%
7. 65.125%

9. .1%

D. 1. 40%
   3. 125%

5. 30%
7. 162.5%

9. 640%

Unit 15 Simple Percent

1. 368.55
3. 14.76
5. 2419.78
7. 170 sheets
9. $55,230; $22,355; $21,040; $2630; $3945; $7890; $11,835; $6575

11. 62.5%
13. 150%
15. 16.2%
17. 15%
19. 81%
21. 900
23. 2000

25. $1125
27. $994.75; $1113.20
29. $309.78
31. $105.05
33. $270.60
35. $139.00

168

Unit 16 Interest

1. $68.48
3. $3478.72

5. (a) $4760;
   (b) $4717.50

7. $1041.63
9. $90.00 gain

Unit 17 Discounts

1. $1.38
3. 35% — $208; 20%, 15% —
   $217.60
   Difference 217.60 −
   208 = $9.60

5. (a) $211.37
   (b) $205.03
7. $125.02

9. $86.43 letterheads;
   $73.63 envelopes

SECTION 5 RATIO AND PROPORTION
Unit 18 Ratio and Proportion

A. 1. 1 to 4
   3. 3 to 1
   5. 1:4

7. 50:127
9. 13 to 30
11. 3 to 4

13. 1/40
15. 6/11

B. 1. 3 1/2
   3. 9.1

5. 2.975
7. 3

9. 5.25

C. 1. 16 picas

3. 21.6 picas

5. Y = 13.125 ounces
   G = .875 ounce
   W = 2.625 = 2 pounds, 10
   ounces

Unit 19 Scaling with the Proportion Wheel

A. 1. 4 7/8"; 150%
   3. 5/8"; 62.5%

5. 12"; 120%
7. 12 13/16"; 183%

9. 5/16"; 62.5%

B. 1. 1 1/2"
   3. 3 5/8"

5. 6 5/16"
7. 9 3/8"

9. 3 3/4"

SECTION 6 MEASUREMENT
Unit 20 Customary Measurement System

A. 1. 5/8"
   3. 1 3/16"

5. 2 1/2"
7. 3 7/8"

9. 6 1/4"

B. 1. 3/4"
   3. 1/4"

5. 1 1/4"
7. 2 3/8"

9. 1 3/4"

C. 1. 1 11/16"
   3. 2 1/16"

5. 13/16"
7. 7/16"

9. 13/16"

D. 1. 43"
   3. 80"

5. 7.02'
7. .8125'

9. 1.556 yd

E. 1. 8 pt
   3. 128 oz
   5. 36 cups
   7. 60 cups

9. 1.6875 qt
11. 1002.24 oz
13. 26.667 cups
15. 18.52 cups

17. 5.44 cups
19. 30.52 qt

F. 1. .172 lb

3. 284.48 oz

5. 412 oz

G. 1. 8.75 sq in
   3. 507.375 sq in

5. 26.60 sq ft
7. 23.375 sq in

9. 41.75 sq in

Unit 21 Metric Measurement System

A. 1. 1.7 cm; 17 mm
   3. 3.1 cm; 31 mm

5. 6.5 cm; 65 mm
7. 10 cm; 100 mm

9. 16 cm; 160 mm

B. 1. 2 cm   5. 3.2 cm   9. 4.4 cm
   3. 0.7 cm   7. 6.1 cm

C. 1. 42 mm   5. 19 mm   9. 18 mm
   3. 51 mm   7. 10 mm

D. 1. 63 mm   5. 15.3 cm   9. 985 mm
   3. 178 mm   7. 573 mm

E. 1. 0.065 L   5. 2,345,000 mL   9. 1800 mL
   3. 2000 mL   7. 3500 mL

F. 1. 3000 g   5. 0.096 kg   9. 85 g
   3. 4.3 kg   7. 9300 g

G. 1. 270 cm^2 5. 3116.75 cm^2 9. 39.35 cm^2
   3. 848.46 cm^2 7. 15.5 cm^2

H. 1. 36.83 cm   5. .48 qt   9. 2.50 kg
   3. 83.82 cm   7. 6.34 cups

Unit 22 The Micrometer

1. .589″   5. .808″   9. .157″
3. .736″   7. .738″

SECTION 7 GRAPHS AND CHARTS
Unit 23 Application of Graphs and Charts

1. (a) $17,500 (b) $22,500   3. (a) 16 hr (b) 7 hr (c) 1.25 hr
   (c) $25,000   (d) 16.5 hr (e) 11 hr

5.

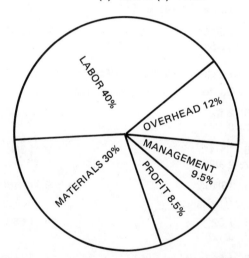

SECTION 8 COPYFITTING
Unit 24 The Point System

A. 1. 24 picas × 22 1/2 picas   5. 3/4 in   9. 51 × 66 picas
   3. 1/12″; 1/2 pica   7. 7 in; 504 points

B. 1. 40 picas   5. 119 picas 9 points   9. 30 picas
   3. 88 picas 7 points   7. 35 picas

C. 1. 18 picas 10 points   5. 2 picas 11 points   9. 11 picas 11 points
   3. 12 picas 9 points   7. 33 picas 9 points

D. 1. 25 picas 6 points
   3. 51 picas 3 points

5. 42 picas
7. 20 picas 3 points

9. 6750 picas

E. 1. 12 columns
   3. 5 picas 7 points with 1/2 point left over

5. 10 columns
7. 63 lines

9. 3456 lines

Unit 25 The Em

A. 1. 22 ems
   3. 15 ems

5. 48 ems
7. 40.5 ems

9. 16.7 ems

B. 1. 6 in
   3. 147 picas

5. 5 in
7. 42 picas

9. 7 1/3 picas

C. 1. 68 picas
   3. 30 picas

5. 75 picas
7. 57 picas

9. 38 picas

D. 1. 189 lines
   3. 54 lines

5. 120 lines
7. 68 lines

9. 90 lines

E. 1. 570 ems
   3. 864 ems
   5. 816 ems
   7. 3600 ems

9. 880 ems
11. 377 ems
13. 2592 ems
15. 684 ems

17. 390 ems
19. 540 ems

Unit 26 Leaded Lines

A. 1. 13 picas 2 points
   3. 29 picas 10 points

5. 9 picas 2 1/2 points
7. 31 picas 6 points

9. 39 picas 8 points

B. 1. 45 lines
   3. 63 lines

5. 16 lines
7. 33 lines

9. 42 lines

C. 1. 832 ems
   3. 4032 ems

5. 10,368 ems
7. 1989 ems

9. 12,919 ems

Unit 27 Fitting Copy to Space and Space to Copy

A. 1. 626 characters

3. 841 characters

B. 1. 2.1405 char/pica

3. 2.5900 char/pica

5. 2.4272 char/pica

C. 1. 116 lines

3. 317 lines

5. 131 lines

D. 1. 43 picas 4 points

3. 52 picas

5. 26 picas 6 points

E. 1. 6 pages

3. 22 pages

5. 5 pages

F. 1. 1368 words

3. 235.6 words

5. 1091.4 words

G. 1. 8/10

3. 6/8

5. 10/12

Unit 28 Cost of Composition

A. 1. $114.14

3. $9.68

5. $7.61

B. 1. $525.26

3. $9591.75

5. $1731.62

C. 1. $173.88
   3. $33.81

5. $23,290.31

7. $76.47

SECTION 9 PAPER STOCK
Unit 29 Packaging Paper

1. 11 packages
3. 120 bundles

5. 20 packages
7. 150 bundles

9. 150 reams; 2 skids

Unit 30 Basic Size, Thickness, and Weight of Stock

A. 1. 17″ × 22″
    3. 20″ × 26″
    5. ply; points

    7. .5 in
    9. 4 points
    11. 5 points

    13. .558 in
    15. 6 points

B. 1. 110; long

    3. 20; long

    5. 65; short

Unit 31 Equivalent Weights

A. 1. 116 lb
    3. 71 1/2 lb

    5. 24 1/2 lb
    7. 54 1/2 lb

    9. 1326 1/2 lb

B. 1. 177 1/2 lb
    3. 160 1/2 lb

    5. 41 lb
    7. 264 1/2 lb

    9. 179 lb

Unit 32 Figuring and Cutting Paper

A. 1. 44 pieces
    3. 21 pieces

    5. 4 pieces
    7. 15 pieces

    9. 16 pieces

B. 1. 65 pieces—5″ grain
    3. 28 pieces—4 3/4″ grain

    5. 56 pieces—5″ grain
    7. 32 pieces—6″ grain

    9. 16 pieces—9″ grain

C. 1. 28 pieces

    3. 14 pieces

    5. 78 pieces

Unit 33 Figuring Most Economical Cut

1. 35″ × 45″
3. 23″ × 35″

5. 22 1/2″ × 28 1/2″
7. 23″ × 35″

9. 38″ × 50″

Unit 34 Determining Number of Sheets Required

1. 550 sheets
3. 770 sheets

5. 917 sheets
7. 477 sheets

9. 8800 sheets

Unit 35 Charging for Cutting and Handling Stock

1. $8.25
3. $17.55

5. $6.45
7. $18.89

9. $15.82

Unit 36 Figuring Weight of Paper Stock

A. 1. 253.7 lb
    3. 67.5 lb

    5. 16.5 lb
    7. 240.6 lb

    9. 58.7 lb

B. 1. 1.28 oz
    3. 2.2 lb

    5. 30.8 lb
    7. 1.2 lb

    9. 5.9 lb

Unit 37 Figuring Cost of Paper Stock

A. 1. $137.38
    3. $11.34

    5. $124.00
    7. $457.93

    9. $17.21

B. 1. $.47
    3. $641.96

    5. $182.41
    7. $2784.24

    9. $32.16

ACHIEVEMENT REVIEW A

1. 181,000 tags
3. $8
5. 2 9/10 reams
7. 23 61/73 shots/hr
9. 2.048 char/pica
11. $1080.63
13. $80.85

15. 20 1/8 sq in
17. 51 picas wide, 66 picas deep
19. 11 columns
21. 56 lines
23. 9072 ems/page
25. 410.4 words
27. 170 reams; 3 skids

29. 109 lb
31. 35 pieces
33. 770 sheets
35. $23.82
37. 211.8 lb
39. $59.14

ACHIEVEMENT REVIEW B

1. 74,410 ems
3. 59 pages
5. 8 11/20 reams
7. 60 pages
9. $2427.13
11. $24.79 gain
13. $983.78

15. 32 21/32 sq in
17. 29 1/4 picas wide by 33 3/4 picas deep
19. 5 picas 9 points
21. 90 lines
23. 11,664 ems
25. 1047.6 words

27. 160 reams; 7 skids
29. 117 lb
31. 21 pieces
33. 688 sheets
35. $31.96
37. 51.3 lb
39. $63.20